MOURLOT. LITH.

EDIBLE

J. CHENANTAIS. J. L. LEMOINE PINX.

Plate 160. *Lactarius pallidus*

NOT EDIBLE

Plate 159. *Lactarius uvidus* (A)
Lactarius flavidus (B)

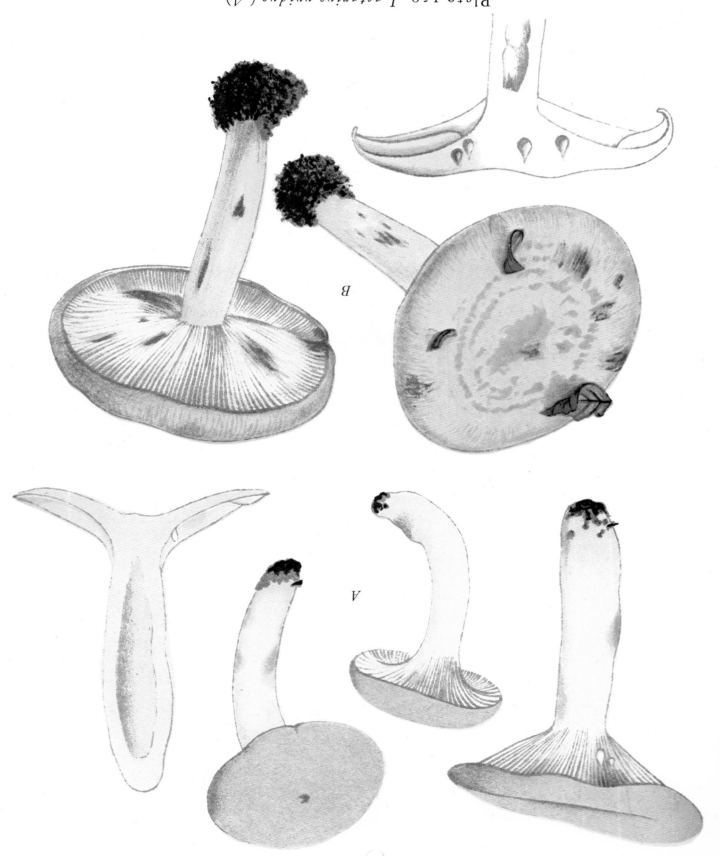

A.BRIDE.PINX.

MOURLOT.LITH.

Plate 158. *Lactarius scrobiculatus*

Plate 157. *Lactarius controversus*

EDIBLE

J. L. LEMOINE ET J. CHENANTAIS PINX.

MOURLOT, LITH.

EXOTIC MUSHROOMS

Text by
Henri Romagnesi

Nouvel Atlas des Champignons

STERLING PUBLISHING CO., Inc. New York

OAK TREE PRESS CO., Ltd. London and Sydney

STERLING NATURE SERIES

Adapted by Rhea Rollin and E. W. Egan

Copyright © 1971, 1970, 1961 by Bordas Editeur, Paris

Published by Sterling Publishing Co., Inc.
419 Park Avenue South, New York 10016
British edition published by Oak Tree Press Co., Ltd., Nassau, Bahamas
Distributed in Australia by Oak Tree Press Co., Ltd.,
P.O. Box 34, Brickfield Hill, Sydney 2000, N.S.W.
Distributed in the United Kingdom and elsewhere in the British Commonwealth
by Ward Lock Ltd., 116 Baker Street, London W 1

Manufactured in
Hong Kong

Library of Congress Catalog Card No.: 79 167659
ISBN 0–8069–3916 8   UK 7061 2336 0
3917 6

Contents

Foreword

THE MUSHROOM has inspired artists since ancient times. Architects have constructed minarets, temples, cupolas, columns in its image. We see its structure in parasols and umbrellas, lids and bells, lamps, coolie hats, and parachutes. Recently, designers have reproduced the familiar shape on fabrics, in salt-and-pepper shakers, and bric-a-brac; jewelers have created expensive pieces based on the mushroom design. One government, Bulgaria, has issued a series of nine different stamps dedicated to the mushroom.

But, strangely, the mushroom itself has seldom been represented in paintings by Western artists. Still life studies by the masters contain apples, pears, peaches, lemons, eggs—even onions—but the mushroom has generally been left out. Perhaps this is understandable. Mushrooms are perishable; their delicate gills and caps change as they dry out on the table. And the champignons that we buy in the market are pale and wan compared to the lush, earthy colors of mushrooms in the woods. As city dwellers, some of us may not have the opportunity to wander and explore the forests, fields and roadsides in search of the wild mushroom, not to eat but to observe. Nor do we have the chance to discover for ourselves that the typical parasol shape is just one of hundreds of different voluptuous patterns and designs to be found among mushrooms. As we study the 160 color plates in this volume, we can just begin to see their individuality—the multitude of delicate yellows, browns, russets and purples, and the subtle shadings, the textures, the sometimes explosive color in these exotic and exquisite plants.

In these pages we can study the paintings and drawings at leisure. The champignons have been captured as they grow, on the ground or on the bark of trees. Hopefully, those of us who have a feeling for art will be inspired by their intricate combination of form, color and line to re-create them in our designs.

—THE PUBLISHERS

Mushrooming

Types of Mushrooms

NATURALLY in a book of this scope we cannot survey in detail and in its entirety such a vast domain as the mushroom world, of which a large part is composed of microscopic organisms, and these only specialists may study. We will limit ourselves principally to those mushrooms which are called, rather inaccurately, higher mushrooms or *macromycetes*, because their size is great enough to permit their being seen with the naked eye. Of the lower mushrooms or *micromycetes*, which do not interest the amateur, we will say only a few words, limiting ourselves to characterizing, very briefly, the larger subdivisions. (Mycetes, by the way, is simply the Greek word for mushrooms.)

Likewise, we will give little attention to the *Myxomycetes*: this is a rather enigmatic group, whose size is often as great as many higher mushrooms, but these are very different in their initial phase. They appear first in the form of a quivering gelatinous mass, not attached to a support and can even be moved. This jelly or *plasmodia*, which seems to be without division, is formed by the fusion of micro-organisms resembling simple animals. It is for this reason that these so-called mushrooms are sometimes grouped in the animal kingdom. But, after a certain time, following a process which has never been traced in detail, the jelly attaches itself to a support and differentiates into reproductive bodies called spores. These are usually formed on the inside of a receptacle with a crisp external membrane, or in sporangia (spore cases), borne upon a little stalk. In this stage, the composition of the membranes which have been formed differs in some respects from all other fungi. The Myxomycetes are common on dead wood, dead leaves, the needles of conifers, etc. The bark-flower is a good example of this.

There are also the *Actinomycetes*, the *Archimycetes* and the *Siphomycetes*. The first are micro-organisms with extremely fine threads, and are not partitioned. The second are sometimes aquatic, sometimes parasites and terrestrial; their vegetative phase is short, and they have zoö-sporangia, organs containing movable spores. The third are composed of an ensemble of unpartitioned threads, and include the *Mucorales*, or molds, and the *Entomophtorales*, parasites of insects.

It is among the *Ascomycetes* (sac fungi) and the *Basidiomycetes* (club fungi) that we find the higher mushrooms. It should be pointed out, however, that each of these two large groups contains orders and families which must be considered micromycetes because of their small size.

The only group we have not touched on are the *Adelomycetes*, which reproduce themselves with cones, and not spores—the *Hyphales, Melanconiales, Spheropsidales*, and other so-called Imperfect Fungi. There are even degraded forms which show no degree of fructification, and simply reproduce themselves by division or offshoots.

In the Ascomycetes, the spores—which, as you know, are the "seeds" of the mushrooms—form on the inside of an enlarged cell called an *ascus* (hence the name Ascomycetes), or a *theca* (spore-case) (Fig. 1A)—where they live until maturity. They are then released into the air, the capsule (theca) opening at the top in various directions (a process called dehiscence). The morels, the helvels, and the Pezizas (Pl. 149 to 154) are examples of the higher Ascomycetes and all may be found in the woods by any admirer of mushrooms.

In the Basidiomycetes, on the other hand, the spores form on the outside of a cell called a *basidium*, to which they are attached by little stems, or *sterigmata* (Fig. 1B). At maturity, they each detach themselves from their sterigma and are projected a short distance. It is among the Basidiomycetes that we find the mushroom shapes most familiar to the public. All mushrooms having gills under the cap, such as the agarics, or pores (*Boletus*, Pl. 118 to 138 and polypores, Pl. 139 to 142), or spines (*Hydnums*, Pl. 143) are Basidiomycetes. So are all those in which the stem is decorated with a ring or has a covering.

In practice, although capsules, spores and basidia may not be observable except under the microscope, it is not difficult to distinguish these two major groups, except in several special cases.

For example, certain Basidiomycetes (Cyphellinae, Aleurodiscus) have a cup form like that of one group of the Ascomycetes: these are most commonly little hairy mushrooms growing on dead stems or wood. Also, underground mushrooms, shaped like potatoes are not all, like the well-known truffle, Ascomycetes—some have basidia. You would not mistake the *Phallus* species (Pl. 146) for one of the morels (Pl. 149), because their stem covering, sticky cap and fetid odor are all lacking in the morels. In addition, several Ascomycetes resemble in their grouped form unbranched Clavarias, which are Basidiomycetes.

Learning to distinguish such mushrooms and putting them in their proper group can be fascinating during a walk in the woods.

The Mushroom's Rôle in the Life Cycle

FUNGI, including mushrooms, make up an extremely large group—more than 100,000 species at the present time, a number which is known, moreover, to be very much below the true one. Generally regarded as plants, fungi vary greatly in outward appearance, but have at least one common characteristic: the absence of chlorophyll. Chlorophyll is the green substance which enables other plants to take directly from the air the carbon dioxide which is indispensable to their growth and nutrition. In the Plant Kingdom, fungi are classified as *thallophytes*, along with bacteria and algae. Unlike the higher plants, they have neither leaves, flowers, nor true roots.

Some authorities, however, are inclined to classify all fungi as organisms that are neither vegetable nor animal, but on the border between the two Kingdoms. The name *Protista* has been proposed for this Third, or Intermediate, "Kingdom."

The practical importance of mushrooms is considerable. Many of the higher mushrooms have a certain nutritive value and are sought by gourmets. No doubt you are aware of the important rôle played in industry by the yeasts, and in medicine by the countless antibiotics of fungal origin: penicillin, streptomycin, etc. In addition to these benefactors of man, there is a whole series of fungi that are formidable enemies of humankind: some are the agents of various illnesses of men and animals (ringworm, for example); others are parasites of cultivated plants (red and black rusts, mildews, etc.); certain higher mushrooms are poisonous and even fatal, and others constitute a grave danger to woodwork, floors, and fence posts, which they can destroy fairly rapidly.

How a Mushroom Grows

Now THAT we have limited our discussion to the Basidiomycetes and Ascomycetes or "higher" mushrooms, we should start by taking a look at their structure.

First let us look at the *mycelium*, the underground organism, of which the mushroom itself is only the fruit. The mycelium results directly from the germination of spores, and consists of a network of extremely fine threads, called *hyphae*. In many cases, it is too fine to be observed, and its parts are spread out beneath the surface of the soil, and under the bark of trees.

However, although invisible, the mycelium may sometimes reveal its presence by its smell, identical to that which the developed mushroom will later give off. If, while walking in mountain pastures, you get a whiff of fresh grain, kneel down, take a fistful of earth and sniff it. You are in an area where the mushroom *Lyophyllum georgii* is common. Come again in the spring, with a large basket. In the same way, an odor of cyanogen gas reveals the presence of a kind of *Clitocybe*. When you are in a grove of beech trees, and you perceive a strong smell of garlic, you may deduce that soon the elegant *Marasmius alliaceus*, or one of its close relatives, will spring up there.

The mycelium may also reveal its presence by the color of the material in which it is embedded. Often you can find fallen oak branches, which seem painted a magnificent blue-green, and not a paint pot to be seen! Well, the green coloration is in reality produced by the mycelium of *Chlorociboria aeruginosa*. Carry home a piece of this "green wood"; place it in moss, carefully keep it moist, and you will one day see a pretty mushroom grow, green like its mycelium. In the same way, pieces of wood "painted" red announce the presence of *Peniophora sanguinea*.

In some instances, the mycelium may be seen directly. In some mushrooms, the threads of the mycelium merge into white cottony sheets at the base of the mushroom. Sometimes the stem is provided with a "sock" of bristly hairs that are actually part of the mycelium (*Marasmius peronatus*, Pl. 102A). Or the mycelium may sometimes form sturdy strings, often branching, which may attain considerable length (more than 30 feet). These are called rhizomorphs, and are typical of *Collybia platyphylla* (Pl. 104). They are present in *Clitocybe mellea*, but are less evident, since they are hidden under the bark of the tree on which the mushroom lives.

In mushrooms growing on wood, dead trunks, and fruits fallen from trees, the mycelium takes a mattress-like shape called a *stroma* (from the Greek word for bed). Among the Ascomycetes, the stroma is often black and strongly colors the substance in which it grows. Less often, the mycelium may thicken into a hard globular or oblong formation, consisting of an external covering or *cortex*, and a softer interior of a whitish hue. This oblong formation is called a sclerotium. This type of mycelium can exist for a long time in an unfavorable environment, waiting to produce its mushroom as soon as the right conditions exist. You can observe this in fungi of the genus *Sclerotinia*. Among the Basidiomycetes, it exists among several species of Coprinus and Collybia. The latter are tiny mushrooms with a whitish cap, and a very thin stem. They often develop upon old mushrooms, which are dried up and blackened, looking as though they had been burnt to a crisp. Look closely, and you may notice that the Collybias grow from tawny, oblong cells, which are none other than sclerotia; in the dry season, you will only find the sclerotia, and you may make them grow in the same way that you did with the Chlorociboria of the "green wood."

Another interesting mushroom found in Italy, is *Polyporus tuberaster*, which has the strange property of producing a mycelium that unites and cements the earth into a rocky mass. In order to see the mushroom grow, it is sufficient to place a piece of this "pietra fungaia" (mushroom stone) in a warm and humid place and to water it lightly. This stone may be moved from one location to another without losing its properties.

In certain cases, it is possible to get the mushroom to spring up by placing its mycelium in a favorable environment: horse manure suitably treated, for the commercially grown field mushroom; old poplar stumps for *Agrocybe aegirita*; and heaps of rotting leaves for the blue-stemmed *Rhodopaxillus nudus*.

How does a mushroom grow? Putting aside the question of reproduction, we may well ask ourselves whether the popular saying, "grow like a mushroom," (which suggests an incredible speed and disconcerting ease of growth), corresponds to any scientific reality.

On this subject, we are more ignorant than informed. Especially about the main point—the *development of the spores* which is the first phase of the life of a mushroom. The higher plants have seeds, which, if sown under the right conditions, will sprout after a definite lapse of time. The spores of the higher mushrooms are not of the same nature. First of all, their ability to grow in various artificial environments declines rapidly and may disappear in several days if the spores are kept dry—and if they are to be kept germ-free, they must be kept dry. Very often, they simply refuse to germinate. Species which grow on rubbish and wood, or whose spore contains a large germinative pore, are in general more likely to germinate. But, even in this latter case, no matter how suitable the environment may be, only a few mushrooms will result from the scattering of countless spores.

From this you may deduce that in Nature the germination of a spore must be an exceptional phenomenon. The quantity of spores produced by a single mushroom in its short life is enormous—in the billions! One authority estimates that the common field mushroom (*Psalliota campestris*) produces about a million spores per minute, which amounts to a billion and a half per day. For species as large as *Ungulina fomentaria* or *Bovista gigantea* (which weighs sometimes up to 10 pounds), you arrive at a literally astronomical figure—in excess of a trillion. If spores germinated as easily as the seeds of flowering plants, the entire earth would be covered with mushrooms, to the point where you would not be able to set foot in the forests!

However, you could dump tons of mushrooms into a particular corner of the forest and let them scatter their clouds of spores—and you might never see a single mushroom appear apart from those that grew there spontaneously!

Once the mushroom gets started it often develops very quickly. Nonetheless its development requires such a series of rare combinations of physical conditions, that its growth ought rather to be considered a kind of miracle! Humidity and temperature certainly play their rôle; a long period of germination is apparently necessary for some species. Very complex questions of nutrition must also be involved. "Thermal shocks," that is, quick changes of temperature, also appear necessary for the germination of certain mushroom species. Unhappily, it is impossible to follow the life of spores in their natural environment, and this is one of the causes of our ignorance on many basic questions.

Assuming that the spore has germinated, it is still necessary that the mycelium develop and not abort. The principal factor in this second phase is the humidity of the soil, dependent mainly on rainfall. A wet spring is necessary in order that a year be good for mushrooms. The temperature also enters the picture, for each mycelium has its "optimum" temperature for growth. Chemical make-up of the soil also plays a primary rôle.

Finally, even if the mycelium has developed properly, the growth of the carpophores, from which the fruiting bodies emerge, is subject to many conditions.

All in all, when mushrooms pop up in the woods and on logs, it is the result of an extraordinarily delicate and precarious process—one hardly compatible with the popular notion of "mushrooming."

Poisonous Mushrooms

A CERTAIN number of higher mushrooms are poisonous, some even fatal. Their number is relatively small—hardly thirty species among the thousands to be found in the woods and fields; but the most poisonous species are, unfortunately, common and a real danger lies in wait for the imprudent gourmet.

First of all, put aside any notion that there are simple tests to determine whether a mushroom unfamiliar to you is safe to eat. Do not give the least credence to the silver coin test (happily, there are hardly any silver coins left!). The coin is supposed to turn black when brought into contact with a toxic mushroom. Too many people have lost their lives as a result of this mistaken belief.

You may have been told if you see a slug nibbling on a mushroom that you may eat it yourself without fear. What you were not told is that slugs can eat the deadly Amanitas, without ill effect. But the same Amanitas will kill you.

If you are told that a mushroom will lose its toxicity if it has been marinated for several days in water and vinegar—do not believe it.

Blanching (plunging briefly into boiling water) may eliminate bitter taste and irritants to the digestive tract, from some mushrooms, but it does *not* eliminate the poisons of the truly dangerous species.

Whether you like it or not, there is only one way to avoid poisoning: to be perfectly familiar with the botanical characteristics of the dangerous species. You should even be able to identify mushrooms without question when they are damaged or imperfectly developed. Above all, you should learn to recognize, in all their various forms and phases, the three fatal Amanitas, *phalloides, verna* and *virosa*—even if their characteristic rings and outer parts have accidentally been destroyed.

Never eat mushrooms that are decomposed or show signs of age. Even harmless species can make you ill if they are too ripe. Do not put poisonous species in the same container with mushrooms you intend to eat—there is some evidence that even the spores of the Amanitas, tiny as they are, can make you ill if they brush off onto an edible mushroom.

The best advice, really, is to leave all wild mushrooms alone, unless you know what you are doing. Admire their form and color, but do not eat them.

Edible Mushrooms

Mushrooms are highly esteemed by gourmets, especially in France, the land of Brillat-Savarin. But are they as nourishing as has sometimes been claimed, and may we regard them as a true "vegetable meat"?

The answer is no. First of all, mushrooms contain a very high proportion of water (82 to 92%), and in this respect resemble such vegetables as cabbage, cauliflower and spinach, which are from 91 to 93% water, against about 87% for carrots and 75% for apples. Mushrooms also contain minerals (0.6 to 1%), sugars and other carbohydrates (1 to 2.7%), and a little fat (0.2 to 0.7%). While the protein content is high, most of the proteins are not even assimilable (from 10 to 30%), and the rest (1.3 to 5.3%) are of inferior value as food! The vitamin content seems a little more valuable, especially Vitamin A in the chanterelle, and Vitamin B1 and D in the boletus (cèpe). In certain species, the presence of Vitamin B2 has been detected, but Vitamin C appears to be lacking, or exists only in the tiniest amounts.

Thus, all the elements of a complete diet are present, which explains why certain experimenters have been able to live entirely on mushrooms for a period of time. But not for too long, because these elements are in very small quantity in the natural state. The elimination of water through drying greatly improves the nutritional value of mushrooms. It has been pointed out that the odorous substances in mushrooms must play a similar rôle to that of spices. According to Pavlov, flat-tasting edibles are neither digested nor assimilated as well as those whose taste is enhanced by some culinary trick. Even so, mushrooms often prove heavy and difficult to digest well, and doctors forbid them to patients suffering from liver complaints.

We should eat mushrooms less to sustain us than to please our palates. That is enough to given them a place in our esteem.

There are a hundred recipes for cooking mushrooms. We can pass tips on only a few of them to you, with the recommendation that you consult one of the innumerable cookbooks available, for full information.

To begin with, choose only very fresh, sound specimens. Avoid as far as possible any washing, peeling, or blanching. Just brush them gently, if you feel you must clean them. Cook them over a low flame, in a covered pan, and not too long. Except in certain special cases, do not use plain metal pans—crockery or Pyrex are preferable, and be sparing with the salt. Salt toughens mushrooms.

Mushroom Omelette

Cook the mushrooms in a separate pan, and, when they are nearly done, quickly beat 6 eggs, as you would for an ordinary omelette and pour them into an omelette pan, which you have already heated to the proper point. Add the mushrooms and cook two minutes.

Mushrooms Sautéed aux Fines Herbes

Cook the mushrooms in a pan over a low flame until most of their water content has been drawn off. Place them in a casserole with butter or two spoonfuls of oil. Add salt, pepper, parsley, scallions and chopped garlic. Serve very hot, with lemon juice.

Mushrooms Provencal

If the mushrooms are very large, cut them into pieces, otherwise leave them as they are. Put two spoonfuls of oil into a casserole and heat, adding salt, pepper, parsley and chopped garlic, then add the mushrooms and let cook gently for ten minutes, stirring from time to time. Then sprinkle with a spoonful of flour, stir well and add two spoonfuls of white wine and a spoonful of water. Let boil ten minutes and serve hot.

Stuffed Mushrooms

Take about a dozen whole mushrooms, clean them and remove the stems. Place two spoonfuls of oil in a pan, then add the mushroom caps, with the gills up. Put on a low flame until the caps start to brown, then remove from flame. Prepare a stuffing—the kind you would use for stuffed tomatoes, fill the mushroom caps with it, and sprinkle with dried bread crumbs. Cook in the oven for twenty minutes.

Mushrooms and Tomatoes

Place a lump of butter in the pan, or two spoonfuls of olive oil, if you prefer. When the oil or butter begins to sizzle, add tomatoes which you have previously cut into fairly thin slices. Let cook about five minutes. Then add mushrooms. Sprinkle the mixture with minced parsley, garlic and shallots. Let cook over a moderate flame for about twenty minutes.

A Word About Mycology

SCIENTIFIC classification is the branch of natural science that enumerates and defines animal and plant species, and organizes them into genera, tribes, families and larger groupings.

This specialized branch is sometimes underestimated, because it seems to be the simplest. The average person is more impressed by any scientist whom he sees surrounded by complicated and bizarre equipment. Is it completely a joke to say today that the kind of awe accorded the atomic physicist is due in part to the imposing size of cyclotrons? Compared to him, what a pitiful figure the naturalist is! The public views him as a mild lunatic who may be met in railway stations or out in the woods. His equipment consists of a humble magnifying glass, and one of those long green boxes similar to the ones carried by plumbers. Sometimes he may carry a net and be mistaken for a shrimp fisherman.

Yet, systematology or scientific classification touches upon considerable biological problems, and is the base upon which all the branches of biology and organic chemistry are built. The Belgian geneticist Vandendries, when elected in 1938 as president of the annual session of the Mycological Society of France, gave, in his inaugural speech, unreserved homage to the science of systematology, defining it as the basis of the entire edifice of the natural sciences.

In mycology, the science which concerns us, classification is a very tricky matter. An animal, or a higher plant, has a definite pattern of positioning itself in nature and has a definite, and a rather limited, habitat. You usually know where to look for it. With mushrooms, what a difference! Their growth seems to be by whim and disconcerts even the most subtle observers—it is almost unpredictable. Indeed, you may count only upon chance to find mushrooms. You must make many unfruitful visits before finding again, in the same forest, under the same tree, on the same stump, the mushroom that you want to see again! There are species that take ten years or longer to find again. A mycologist may spend fifteen years (or a lifetime) before he has had a chance to study alive most of the species of a given genus. Many genera of mushrooms include over a hundred species!

Unlike naturalists who study insects or flowering plants, the mycologist does not have the advantage of being able to work on preserved specimens. In mycology, nothing can replace the examination of the living mushroom in the spot where it grows, because many characteristics essential for distinguishing one species from another disappear entirely in the dry state. Even samples conserved in alcohol or formaldehyde are of dubious value. In view of this, it is no wonder that the study of tropical mushrooms is still in its first stages!

You now see how mycology is, in matters of classification, deprived of a great number of methods which have permitted other branches of natural history to make rapid progress. You will thus not be surprised to learn that even today, all the species which grow in Europe, in France, even around Paris, are far from being fully understood.

Scientific mycology in fact only dates from the end of the eighteenth century. A Dutchman, Christian Hendrick Persoon; a Frenchman, Pierre Bulliard; and a German, Jacob Schaeffer, are the founding fathers of mycology. Next comes the true founder of mushroom classifica-tion, the Swede Elias Fries who, from 1821 to 1877, in a whole series of fundamental works, provided the basis of the classification and enumeration of fungal species. Among French mycologists the dominant figure is Lucien Quelet, who contributed greatly to the study, and his *Mycologiae Flora* remains, along with the *Hymenomycetes Europaei* of Fries, one of the great classics of the science of higher mush-rooms.

Charts

The mushroom fancier with a microscope will find endless diversion in examining the different forms and shapes of the tiny spores and specialized organs of these curious plants. The diagrams which follow should help identify these various minute parts. The number of each diagram corresponds to number of a color plate and represents details of the species depicted on the plate.

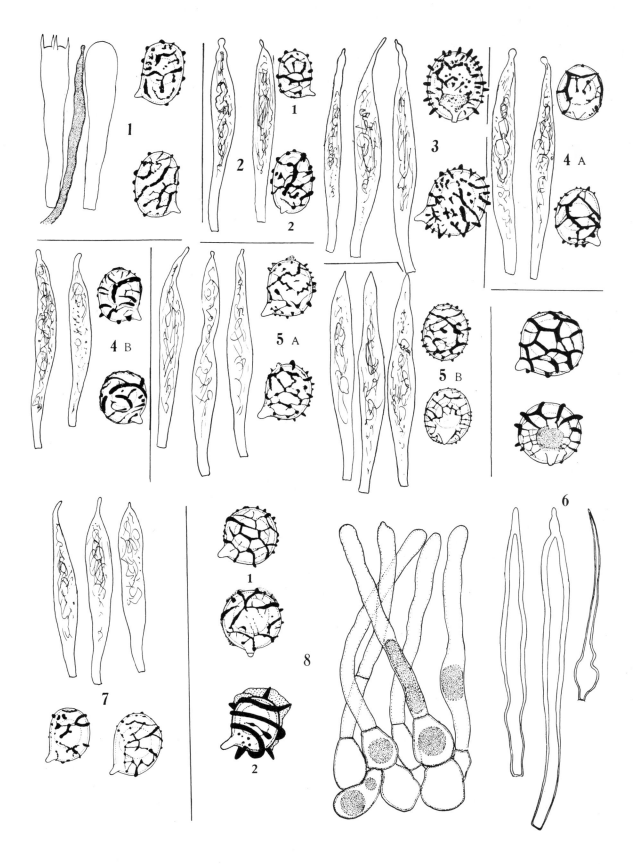

CHART I

1. Spores and a pseudo-cystidium between two basidia.   2. Spores and cystidia (1, species), (2, var. *sublateritius*).   3. Spores and cystidia.   4A, 4B, 5A, 5B. Spores and cystidia.   6. Top, spores; bottom, left and right, a hair from the lining of the cap.   7. Cystidia and spores.   8. (1, spores of species); (2, spore of var. *pterosporus*); right, cross-section of skin of the cap.

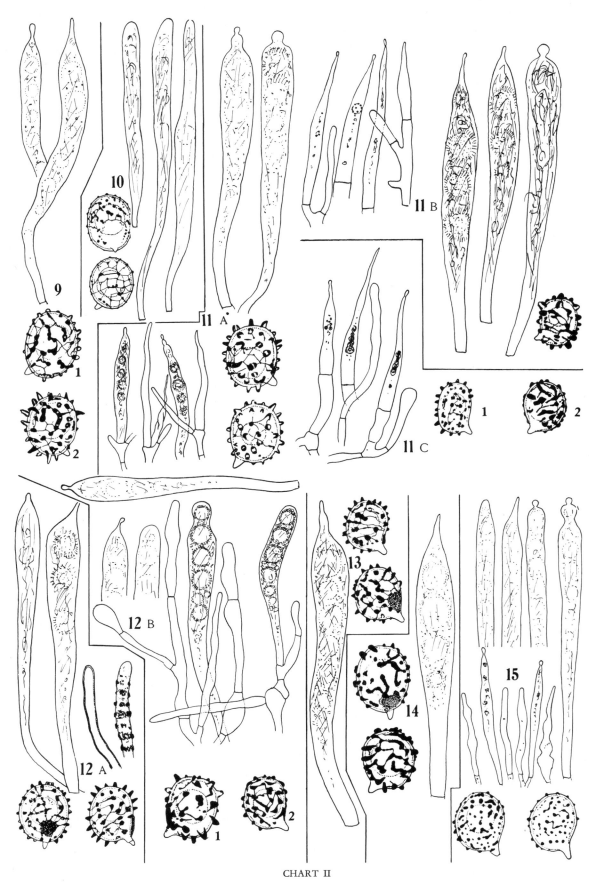

CHART II

9. Cystidia and, bottom, spores. (1, species); (2, var. *chloroides*).   10. Spores and cystidia.   11A. Top, cystidia; bottom, left, elements of the skin of the cap with dermatocystidia; right, spores.   11B. Left, hairs and dermatocystidia from the skin of the cap; right, cystidia with a spore.   11C. Left, hairs and dermatocystidia from skin of the cap; right, (1) spore of var. *amoenolens*; right, spore of species. Cystidia are same as 11B.   12A. Cystidia, right; hairs from skin of cap; bottom, spores.   12B. Top, a cystidium and tips of two others; hairs and dermatocystidia, var. *mairei*; bottom (1), a spore of species and (2), of var. *mairei*.   13. A cystidium and spores.   14. Spores and a cystidium.   15. Cystidia, elements of the skin of the cap, with narrow dermatocystidia and spores.

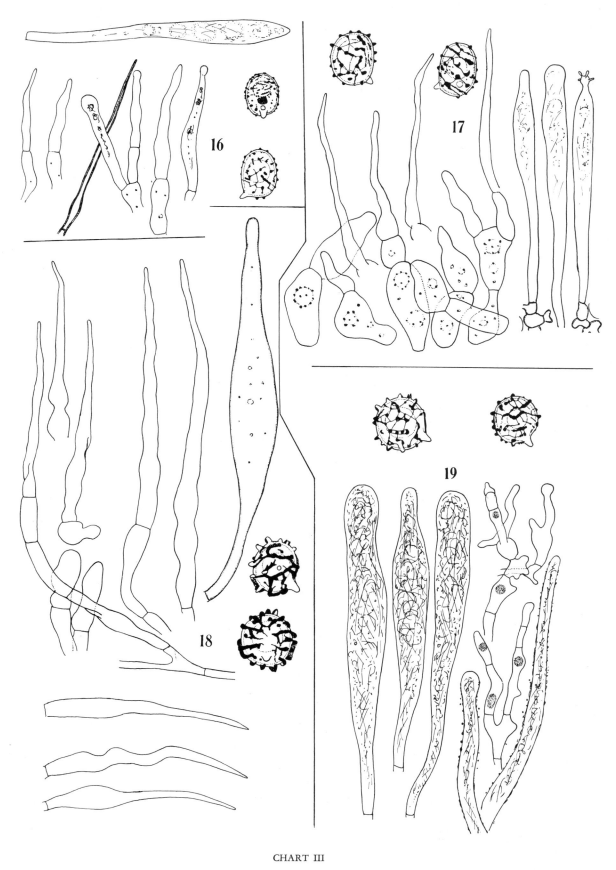

CHART III

16. Elements of skin of cap with a thick-walled, pigmented hair and two dermatocystidia, and spores.   17. Above, spores, cross-section of skin, and, at right, cystidia.   18. Left, hairs; right, a cystidium and spores; bottom, hairs from the gills.   19. Top, spores; bottom, left, cystidia, and right, hairs from skin of cap and dermatocystidia.

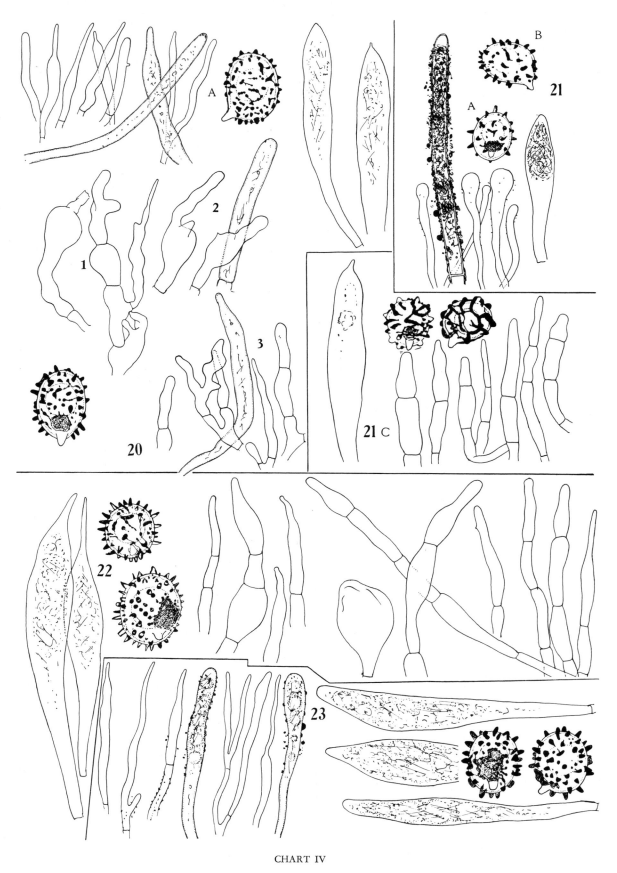

CHART IV

20A. Elements of skin and spore of var. *erythropoda*; right, cystidia. (1, 2 and 3), various types of hairs; bottom, left, a typical spore.   21A and B. Elements of skin, a hypha and a cystidium; (A) spore of *R. vitellina* and (B), of *chamaeleontina*.   21C. Left, a cystidium; middle, spores; bottom, hairs of skin of cap. 22. Left, cystidia; middle, spores; right, hairs.   23. Hairs and dermatocystidia; middle, cystidia, and right, spores.

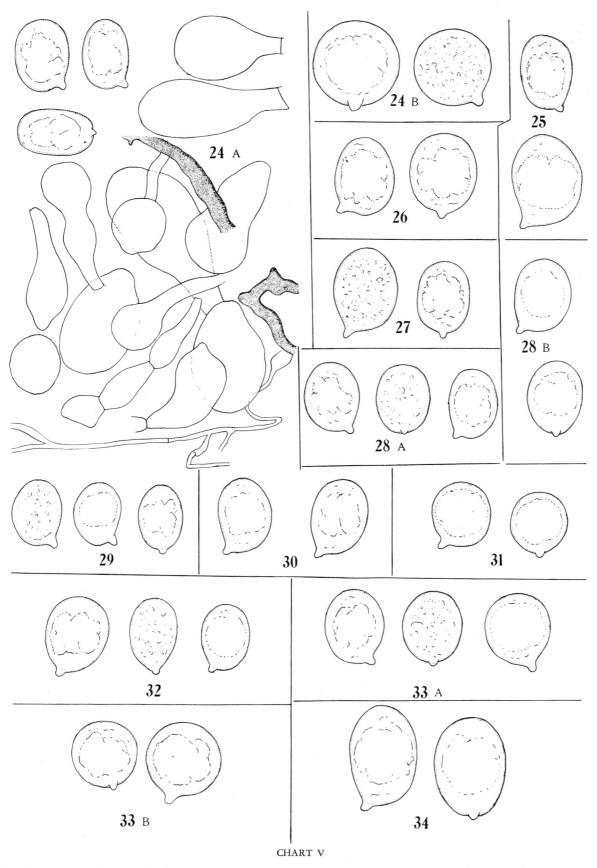

CHART V

24A. Top, left, spores and right, marginal cells; bottom, elements of the universal veil and scales of the cap with 2 laticiferous cells.   24B, 25, 26, 27, 28A, 28B, 29, 30, 31, 32, 33A, 33B, 34. Spores.

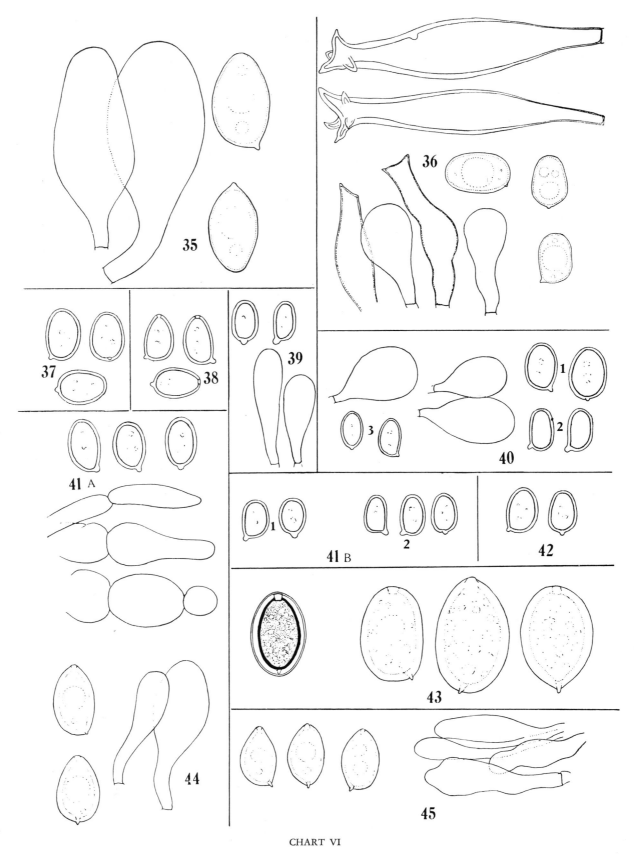

CHART VI

35. Cystidia and spores.   36. Cystidia; bottom left, marginal cells; right, spores.   37, 38. Spores.   39. Spores and marginal cells.   40. Top, marginal cells; (1), spores of species; (2), spores of var. *abruptibulba*; and (3), of var. *silvicola ss. Moeller*.   41A. Top, spores; bottom, marginal cells.   41B. (1), leaf-shaped spores; (2), spores in the shape of resinous drops.   42. Spores.   43. Spores; at left is cross-section of a spore, showing the different membranes and the germinative spore.   44, 45. Spores and marginal cells.

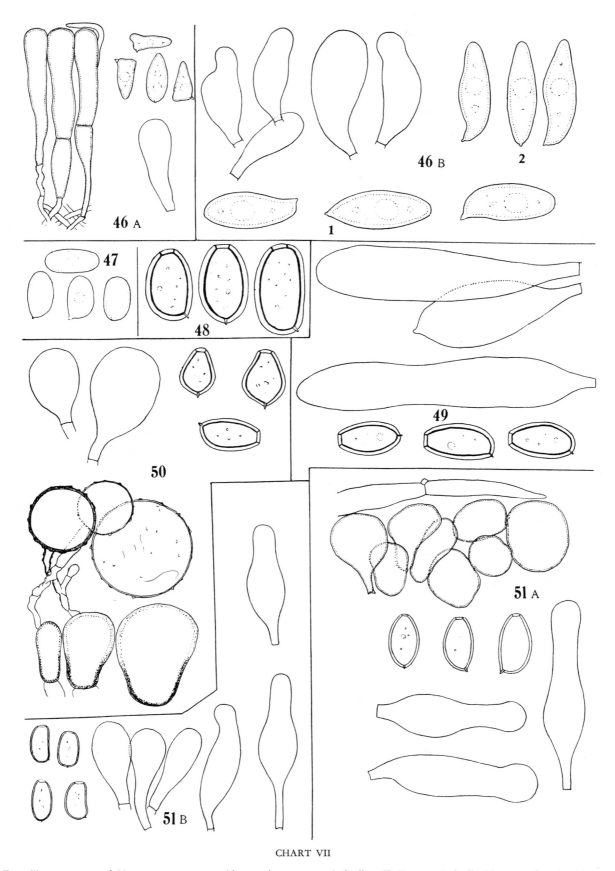

CHART VII

46A. Fence-like arrangement of skin components; spores with spurs; bottom, a marginal cell. 46B. Top, marginal cells; (1), spores of species; (2) spores of var. *metulaespora*. 47. Spores. 48. Spores. 49. Top, marginal cells; middle, a surface cystidium enlarged 500 times; bottom, spores. 50. Left, marginal cells enlarged 500 times; right, spores; spherocytes of the veil, above skin cells. 51A. Cross-section of skin with a hypha of the universal veil; middle, spores; bottom right, marginal cystidia. 51B. Left, spores; middle, club-shaped marginal cells; top, right, surface cystidia.

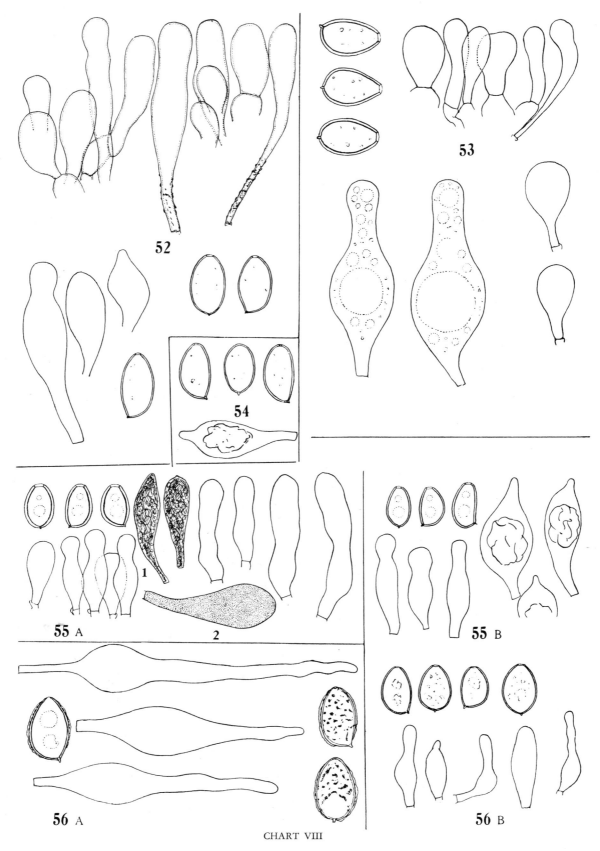

CHART VIII

52. Top, components of the skin; left, cystidia; bottom and right, spores. 53. Top, spores and components of the skin; bottom left, surface cystidia; right, marginal cells. 54. Spores and a surface cystidium. 55A. Top, spores; (1), marginal hairs and (2), surface cystidia; left, marginal hairs and cystidium of a variety. 55B. Spores; left, marginal cells; right, surface cystidia. 56A. Cystidia (surface and marginal); left, spore seen in cross-section; right, spores. 56B. Spores and marginal cells.

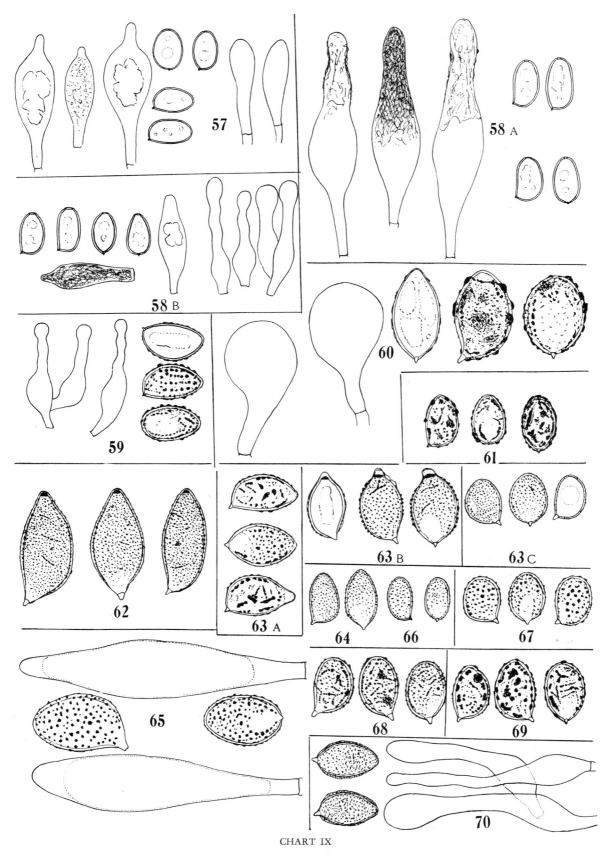

CHART IX

57. Left, surface cystidia; middle, spores; right, marginal cells, among the cystidia.   58A. Cystidia and spores.   58B. Spores; right, marginal hairs; bottom and middle, surface cystidia.   59. Marginal cells and spores, top one seen in cross-section.   60. Marginal cells and spores, one seen in cross-section.   61, 62, 63A. Spores.   63B. Spores (ones at left in cross-section), var. *amoenolens*.   63C, 64. Spores.   65. Top and bottom, cystidia; middle, spores.   66, 67, 68, 69. Spores.   70. Spores and marginal cells.

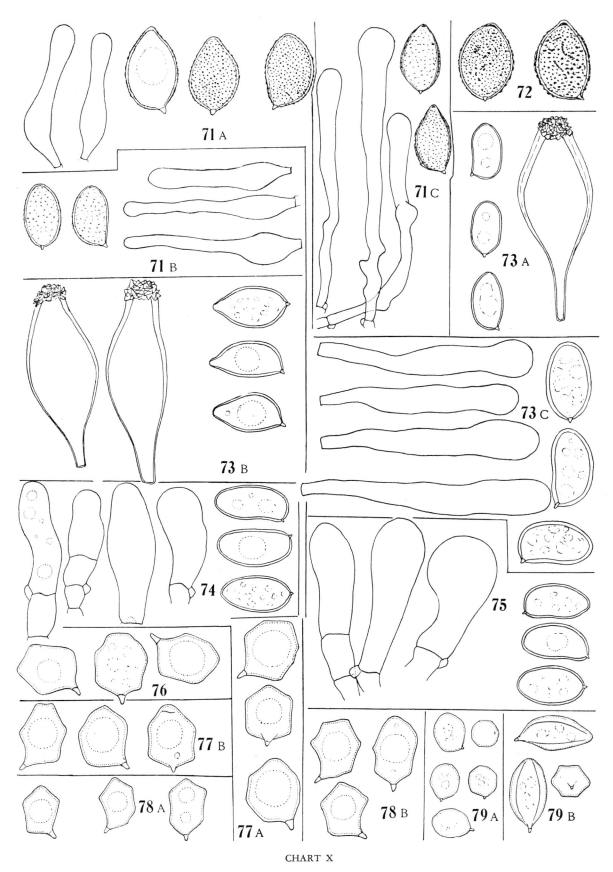

CHART X

71A, 71B. Spores and marginal cells.   71C. Marginal cells and spores.   72. Spores. 73A. Spores and a surface cystidium.   73B. Surface cystidia and spores.
73C. Left, marginal cells; right, spores.   74. Marginal cells and spores.   75. Left, marginal cells and right, spores.   76, 77A, 77B, 78A, 78B, 79A. Spores.
79B. Spores, one at right seen from the lower end.

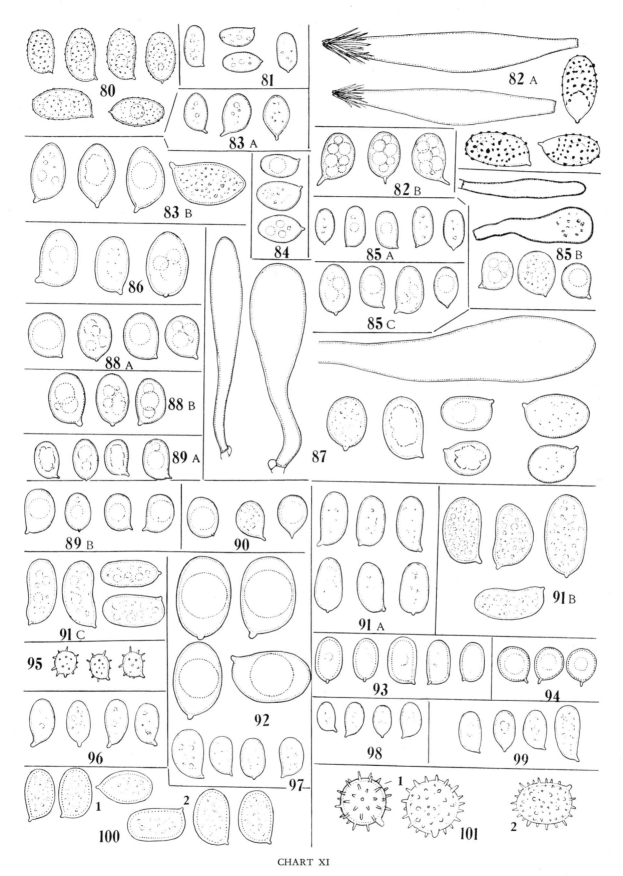

CHART XI

80, 81. Spores. 82A. Cystidia and spores (after G. Metrod). 82B, 83A, 84, 85A. Spores. 85B. Top, marginal cells; bottom, spores. 85C, 86. Spores.
87. Marginal cells. 88A, 88B, 89A, 89B, 90, 91A, 91B, 92, 93, 94, 95, 96, 97, 98, 99. Spores. 100. Spores (1), leaf-shaped; (2), shaped like conifers. 101.
Spores; (1) spores of species; (2), a spore of var. *proxima*.

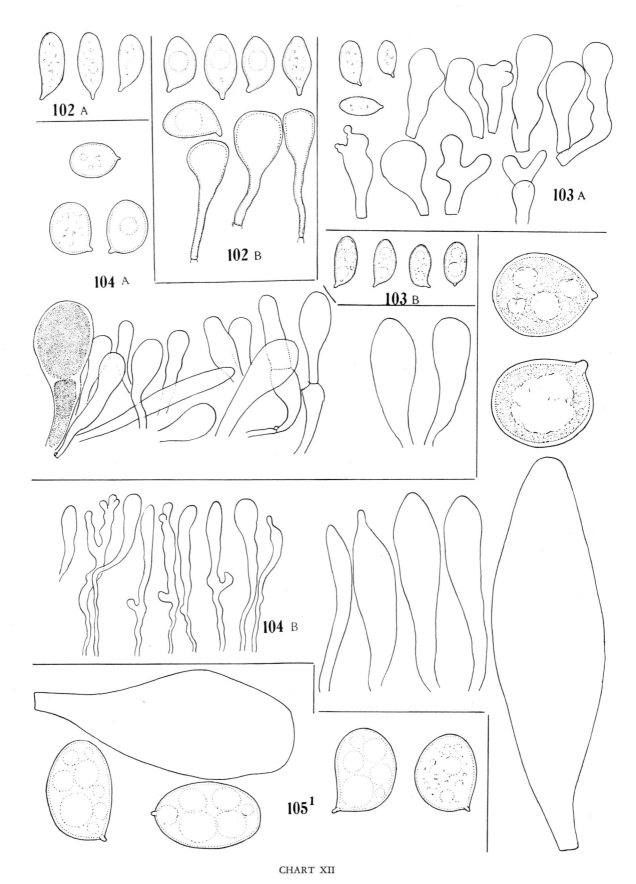

CHART XII

102A. Spores. 102B. Top, spores; bottom, arrangement of skin components. 103A. Top, left; spores; others, marginal cells. 103B. Spores. 104A. Top left, spores; bottom left, hairs of skin; right, marginal cells (not numerous in this species). 104B. Left, fence-like arrangement of cells of cap; middle, marginal cells; left, a surface cystidium and, below, spores. 105[1]. A cystidium and spores.

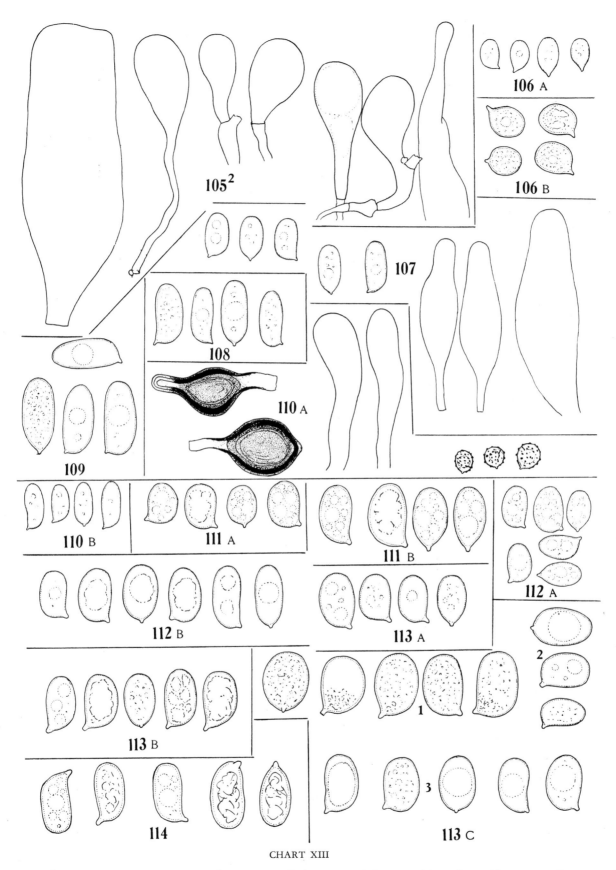

CHART XIII

105². Left, surface cystidium; right, components of skin of cap. 106A, 106B. Spores. 107. Left, spores; right, surface cystidia. 108, 109. Spores. 110A. Left, chlamydospores or conidia from the surface of the stem: middle, pseudocystidia; bottom, right, spores. 110B, 111A, 111B, 112A, 112B, 113A, 113B, 113C, 114. Spores.

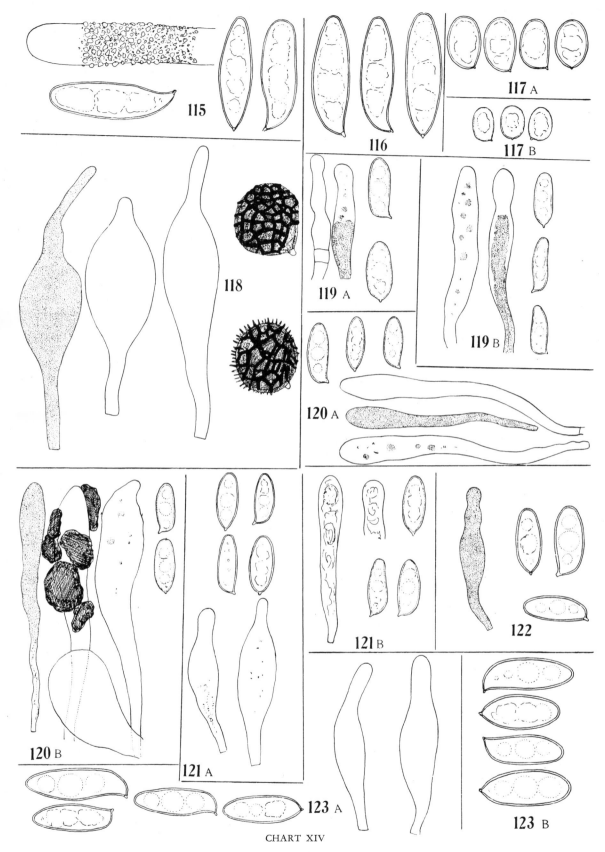

CHART XIV

115. Top, tip of a surface cystidium. 116. Spores. 117A, 117B. Spores. 118. Surface cystidia and spores. 119A, 119B. Surface cystidia and spores. 120A. Spores and cystidia from the tube orifices. 120B. Cystidia from tube orifice (one still has fragments of the veil) and spores. 121A. Spores and surface cystidia. 121B. Surface cystidium and the tip of another (not very distinct from basidia) and spores. 122. A surface cystidium and spores. 123A. Bottom, spores, and right, surface cystidia. 123B. Spores.

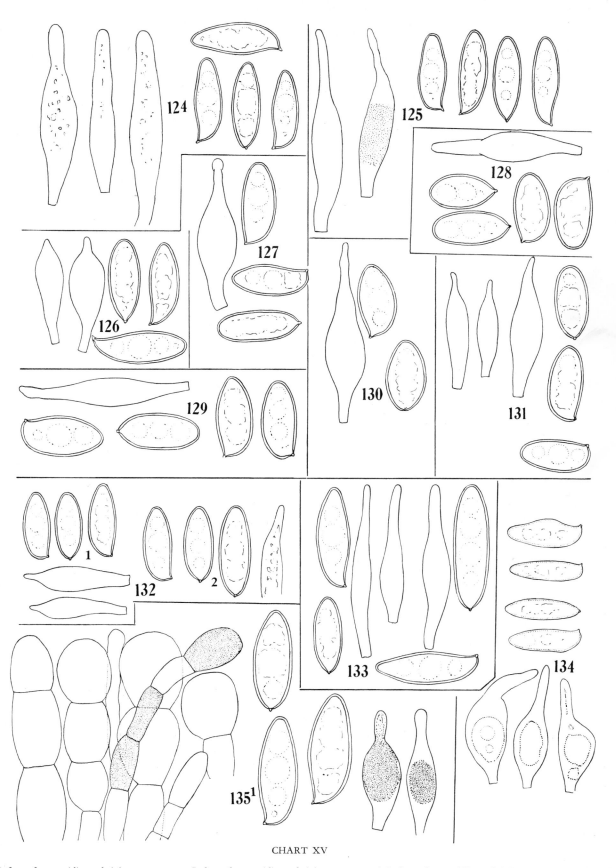

CHART XV

124. Left, surface cystidia, and right, spores. 125. Left, surface cystidia, and right, spores. 126. Left, surface cystidia, and right, spores. 127. A surface cystidium and spores. 128, 129. Top, a surface cystidium and spores. 130. A surface cystidium and spores. 131. Surface cystidia and spores. 132. (1), spores and surface cystidia; (2), spores and tip of a surface cystidium, var. *rhodoxanthus*. 133. Spores of var. *reticulatus*; cystidia: two at left of species, one at right, of var. *reticulatus*. 134. Top, spores; bottom, surface cystidia. 135[1]. Skin of cap, spores and surface cystidia.

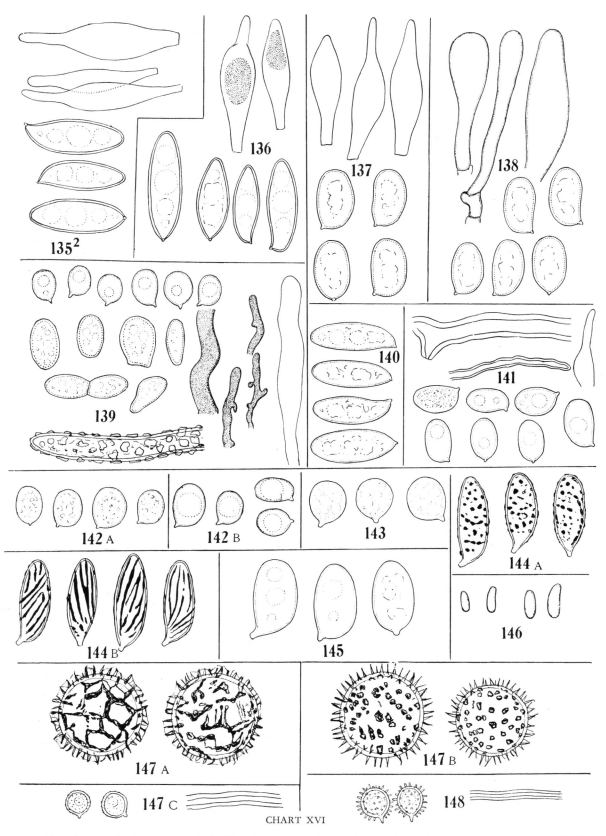

CHART XVI

135². Surface cystidia and spores of *B. leucophaeus*. 136. Cystidia and spores. 137. Top, surface cystidia, and bottom, spores. 138. Top, cystidia from tube orifice, and bottom, spores. 139. Top, spores; below them, conidia produced by the cap; bottom, a hair from the cap; middle, a short section of a laticiferous cell, and right, pseudocystidia and a cystidium from tube orifices. 140. Spores. 141. Top, hyphae, the upper one from the flesh of the cap, the lower from tube tissue; right, a cystidiolum; bottom, spores. 142A, 142B, 143, 144A, 144B, 145. Spores. 146. Spores, after Pilát and Usak. 147A. Spore. 147B. Spores. 147C. Left, spores; right, a fragment of a filament of the capillitium. 148. Left, Spores; right, a fragment of a filament of the capillitium.

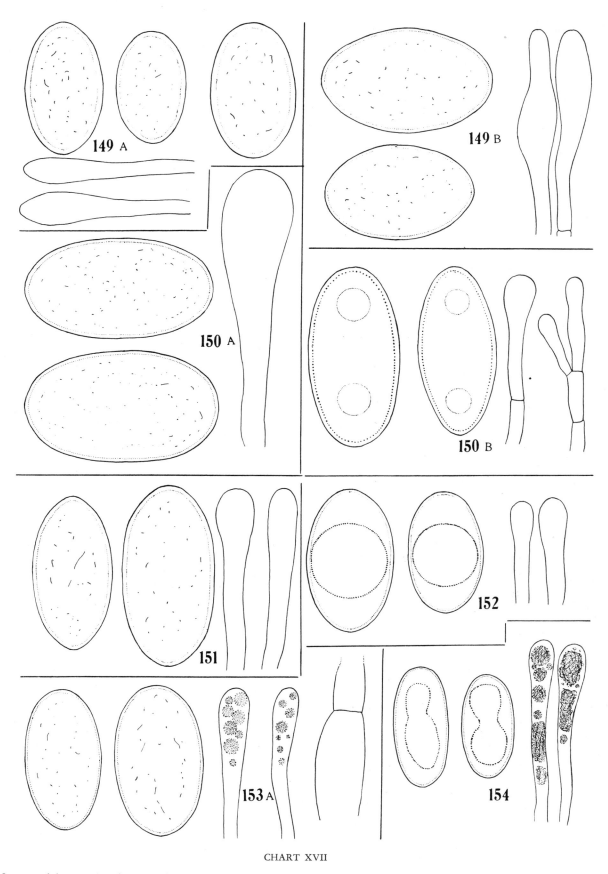

CHART XVII

149A. Spores, and, bottom, tips of two paraphyses (sterile filaments). 149B. Spores, and tips of two paraphyses. 150A. Spores and tip of a paraphysis. 150B, 151, 152. Spores and tips of two paraphyses. 153A. Spores; middle, tips of paraphyses, and left, swollen segment of lower part of a paraphysis. 154. Spores and tips of paraphyses.

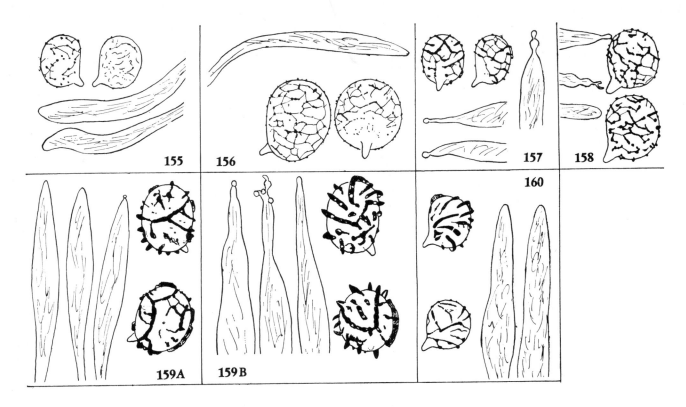

CHART XVIII

155. Top, spores; bottom, cystidia. 156. Bottom, spores; top, a cystidium. 157. Top, left, spores; bottom, right, tips of cystidia. 158. Right, spores; left, cystidia. 159A. Right, spores; left, cystidia. 159B. Right, spores; left, cystidia. 160. Left, spores; right, cystidia.

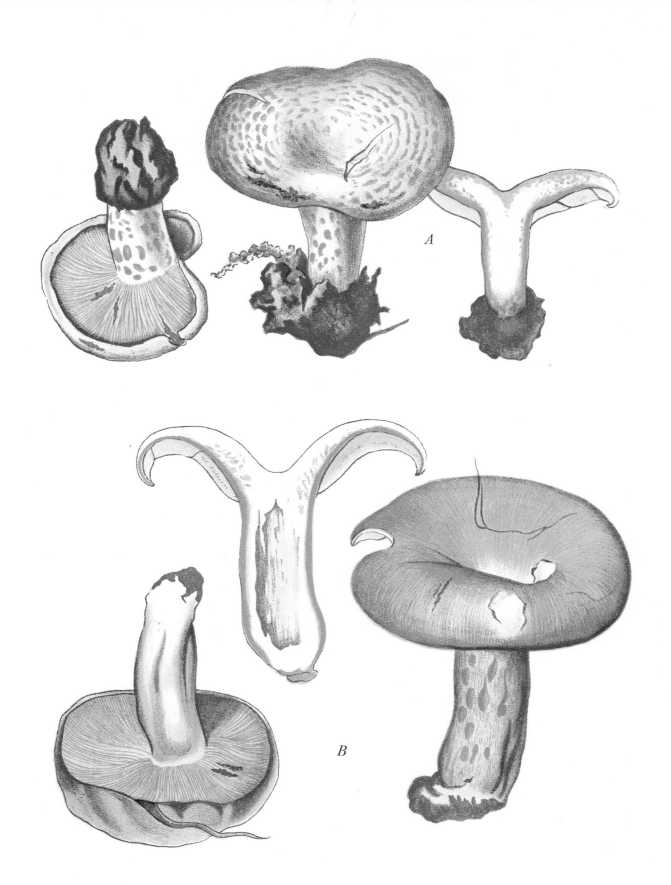

Plate 1. *Lactarius deliciosus* (*A*)
Variety (*B*)

EDIBLE

Plate 2. *Lactarius torminosus* (*A*)
Variety, *sublateritius* (B)

NOT EDIBLE

Plate 3. *Lactarius zonarius*

NOT EDIBLE

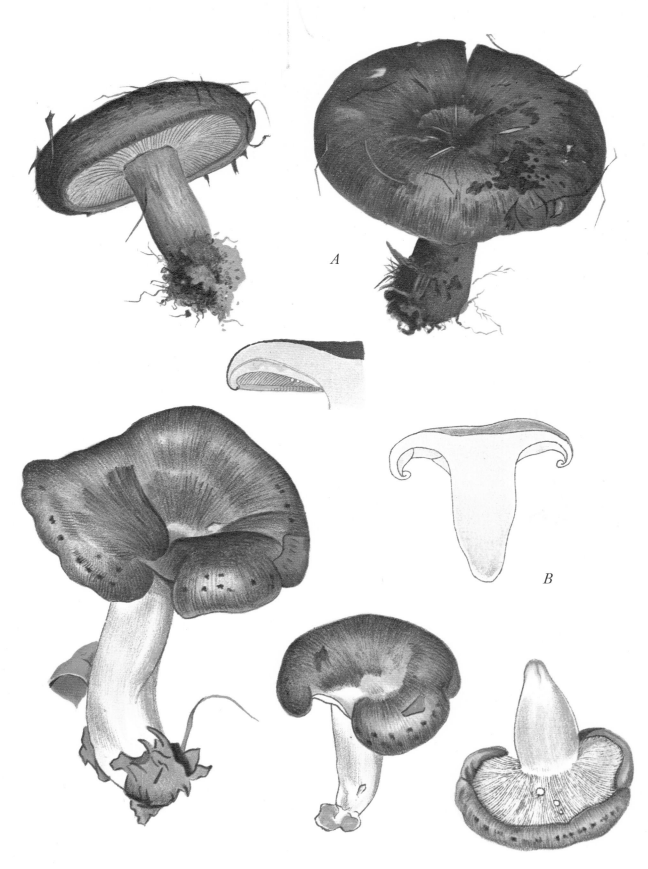

Plate 4. *Lactarius turpis* (*A*)
Lactarius blennius (B)

NOT EDIBLE

Plate 5. *Lactarius mitissimus* (*A*)

EDIBLE

Lactarius chrysorrheus (B)

NOT EDIBLE

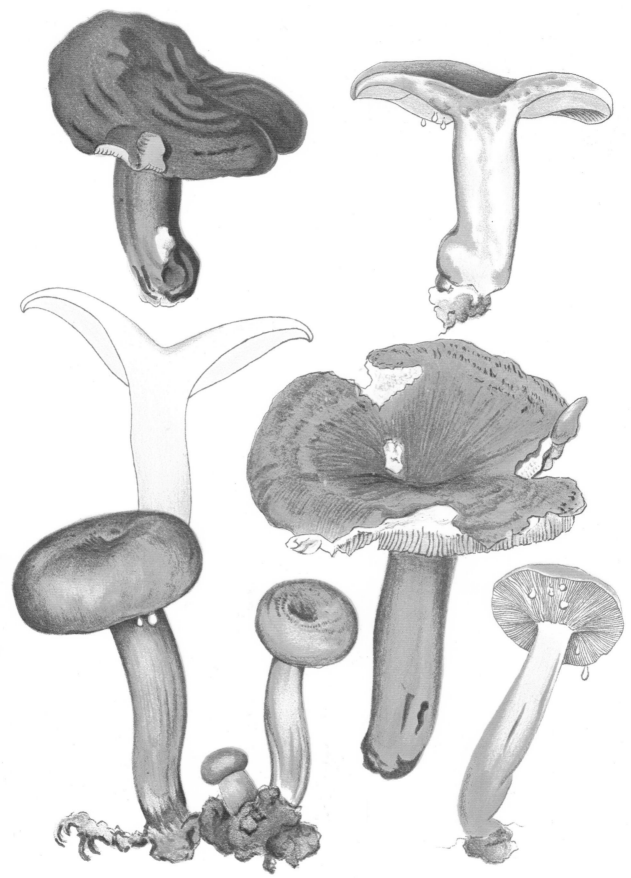

Plate 6. *Lactarius volemus*

EDIBLE

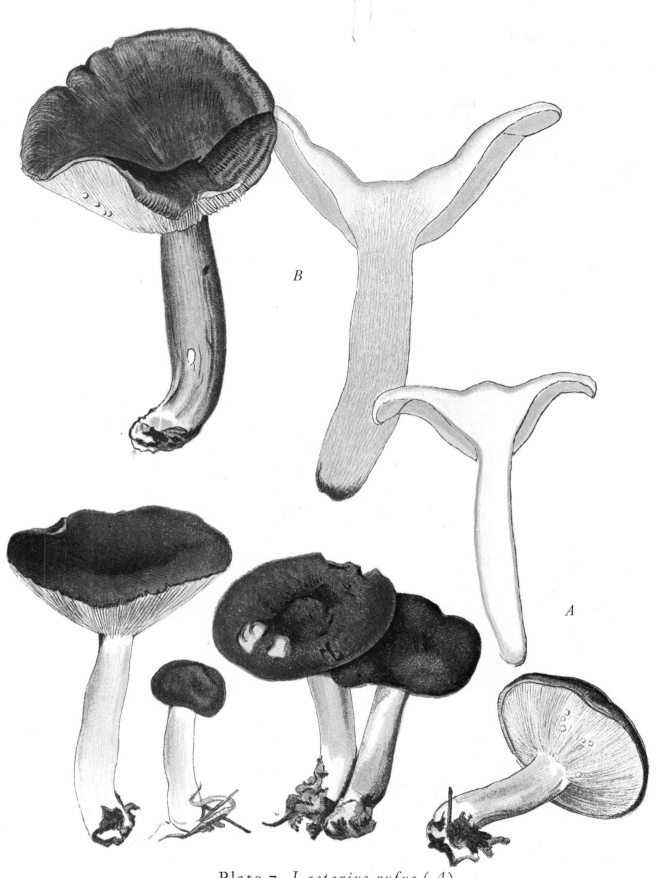

Plate 7. *Lactarius rufus* (*A*)
Variety, *exumbonatus* (*B*)

NOT EDIBLE

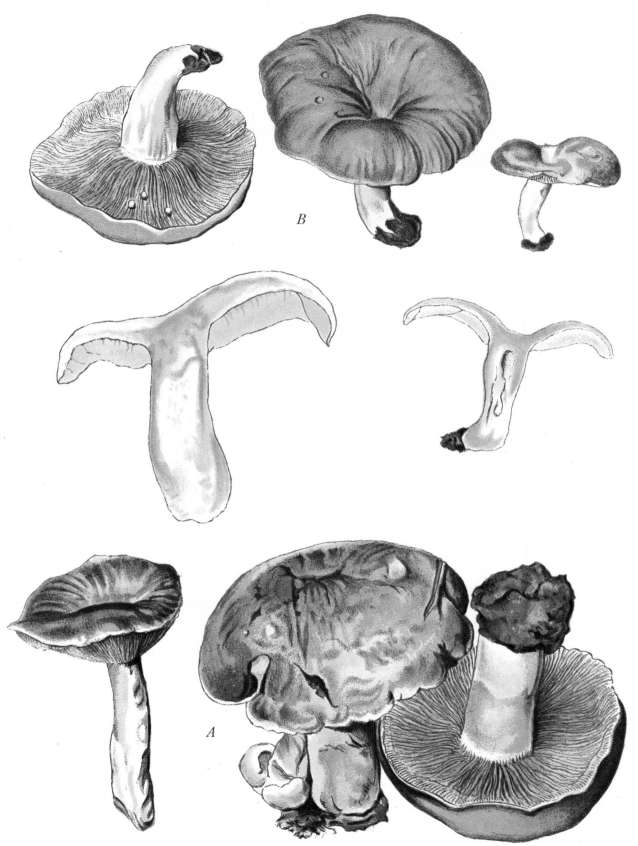

Plate 8. *Lactarius fuliginosus* (*A*)
Variety, *pterosporus* (B)

NOT EDIBLE

Plate 9. *Russula delica*

EDIBLE

Plate 10. *Russula nigricans*

EDIBLE

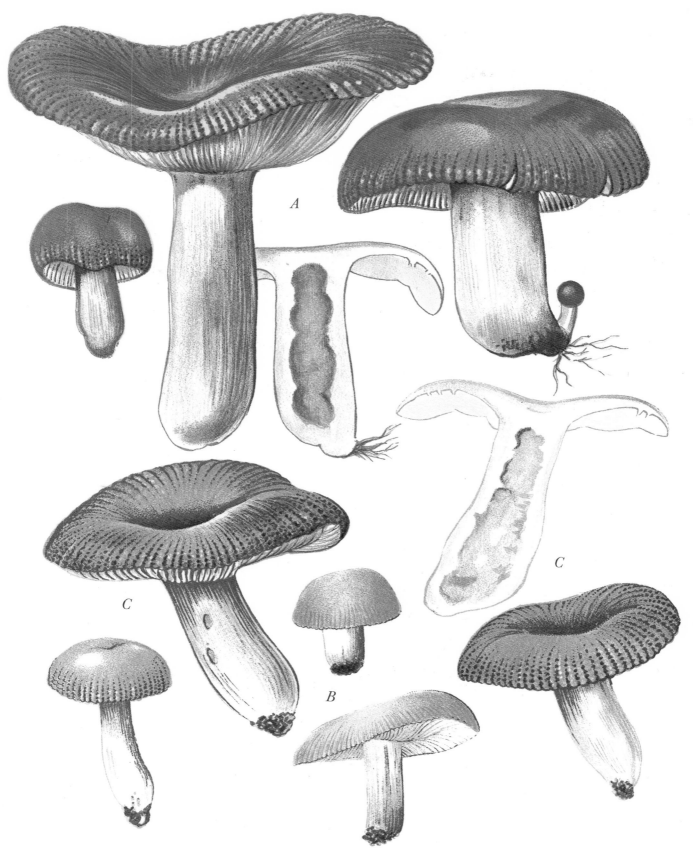

Plate 11. *Russula foetens* (*A*)
Russula pectinata (B)
Russula sororia (C)

NOT EDIBLE

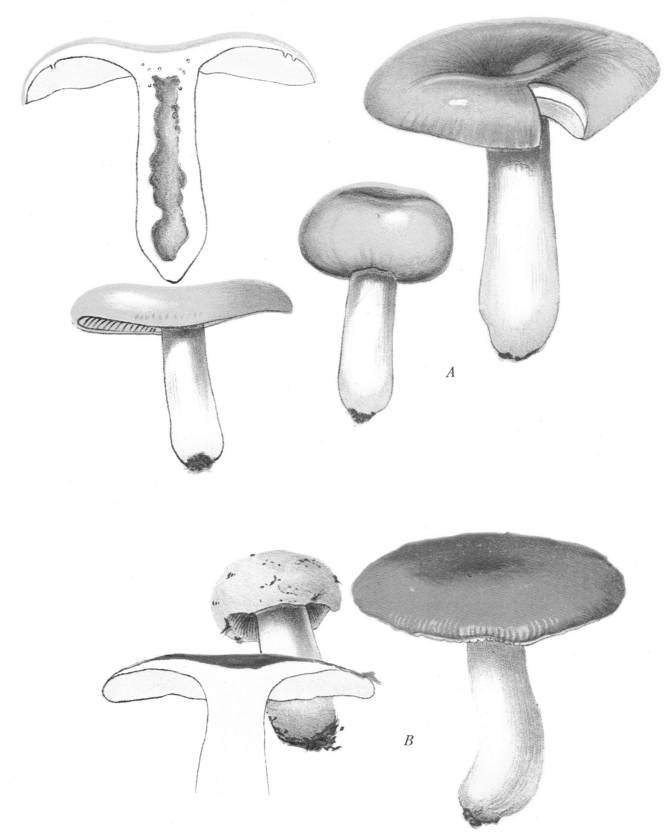

Plate 12. *Russula ochroleuca* (*A*)
Russula emetica (B)

NOT EDIBLE

Plate 13. *Russula sardonia*

NOT EDIBLE

Plate 14. *Russula maculata*

NOT EDIBLE

Plate 15. *Russula cyanoxantha*

EDIBLE

Plate 16. *Russula vesca*

EDIBLE

Plate 17. *Russula virescens*

EDIBLE

Plate 18. *Russula amoena*

EDIBLE

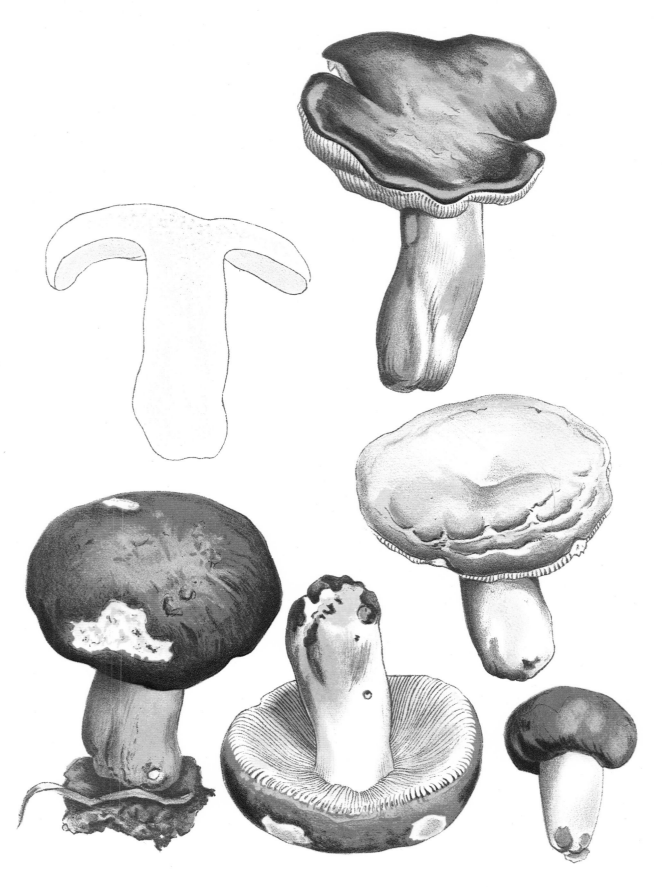

Plate 19. *Russula lepida*

NOT EDIBLE

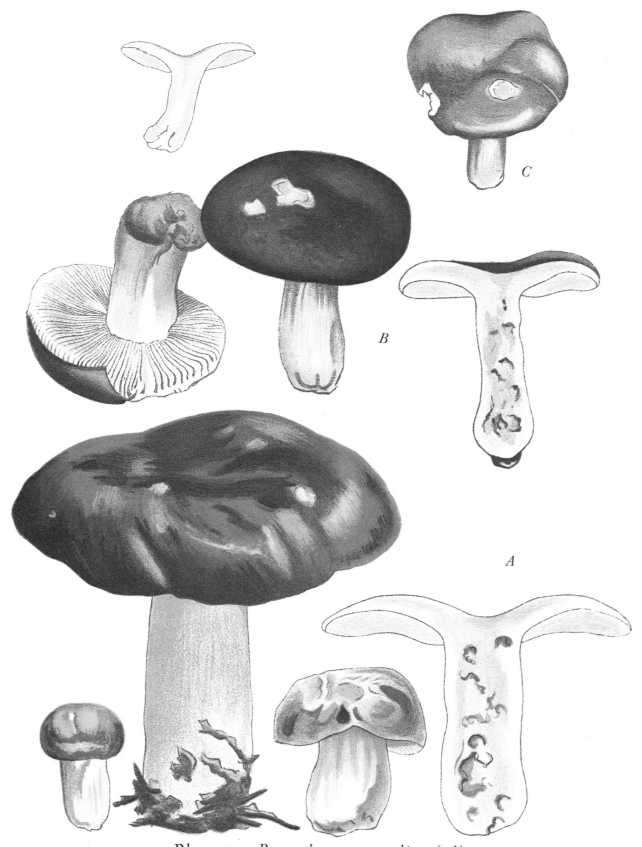

Plate 20. *Russula xerampelina* (*A*)
Variety, *erythropus* (B)
Variety, *olivascens* (C)

EDIBLE

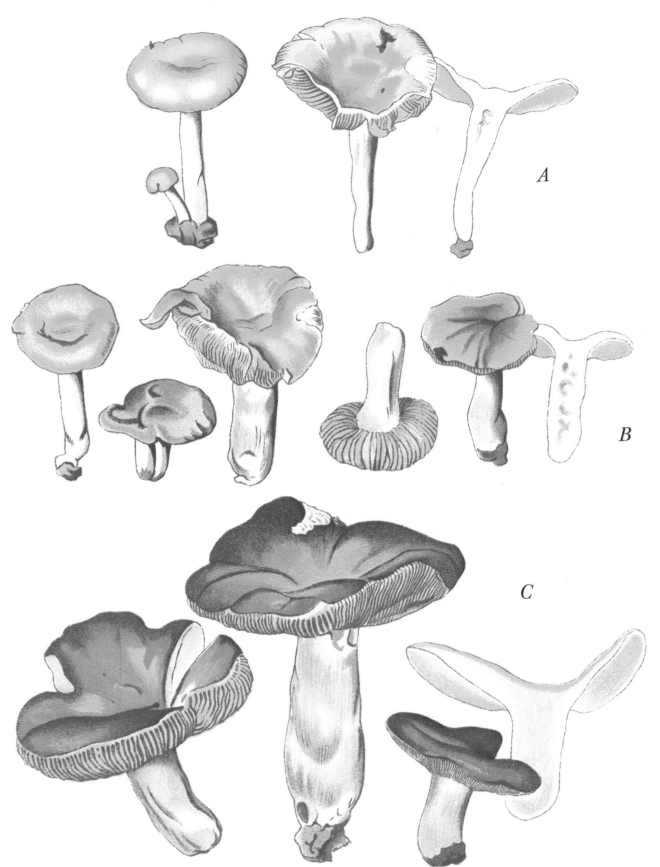

Plate 21. *Russula vitellina* (*A*)
Variety, *chamaeleontina* (B)
Variety, *aurata* (C)

EDIBLE

Plate 22. *Russula olivacea*

EDIBLE

Plate 23. *Russula integra*

EDIBLE

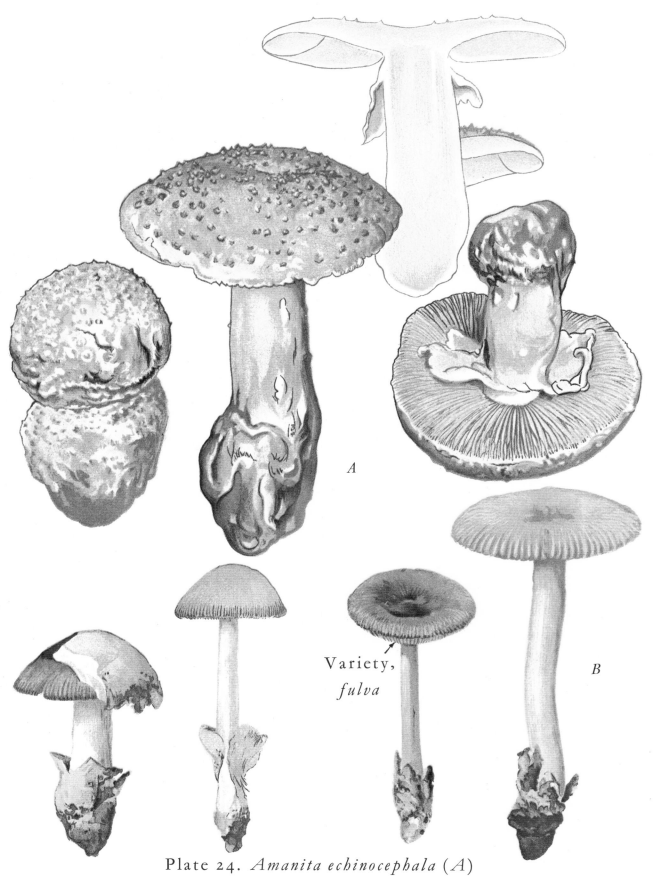

Variety,
fulva

A

B

Plate 24. *Amanita echinocephala* (*A*)
Amanita vaginata (B)

EDIBLE

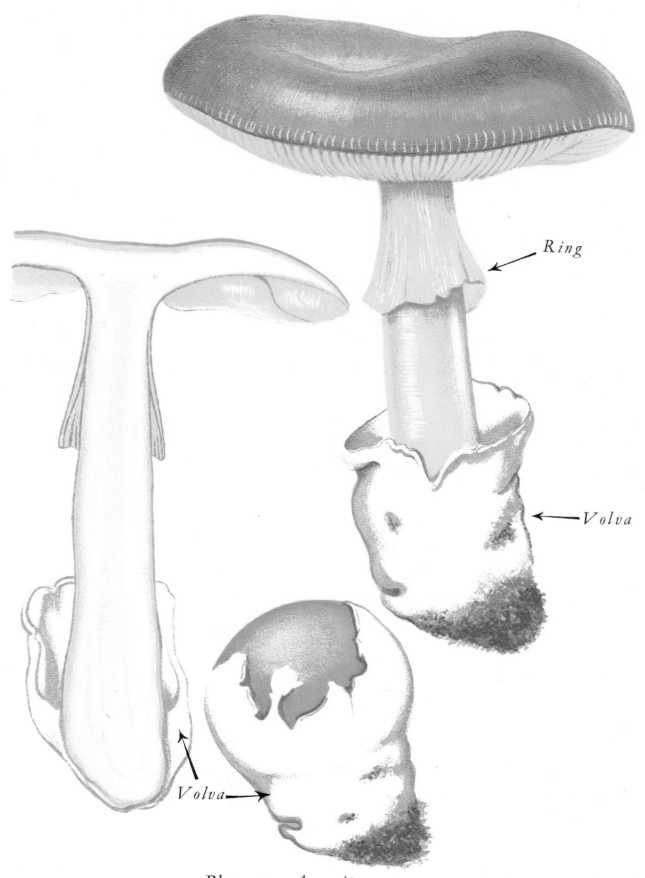

Ring

Volva

Volva

Plate 25. *Amanita caesarea*

EDIBLE

Plate 26. *Amanita muscaria*

NOT EDIBLE

Plate 27. *Amanita gemmata*

NOT EDIBLE

A

B

Plate 28. *Amanita pantherina* (*A*)

NOT EDIBLE

Amanita spissa (B)

EDIBLE

60

Plate 29. *Amanita rubescens*

EDIBLE

Plate 30. *Amanita ovoidea*

EDIBLE

Plate 31. *Amanita citrina*

EDIBLE

Plate 32. *Amanita phalloides*
NOT EDIBLE

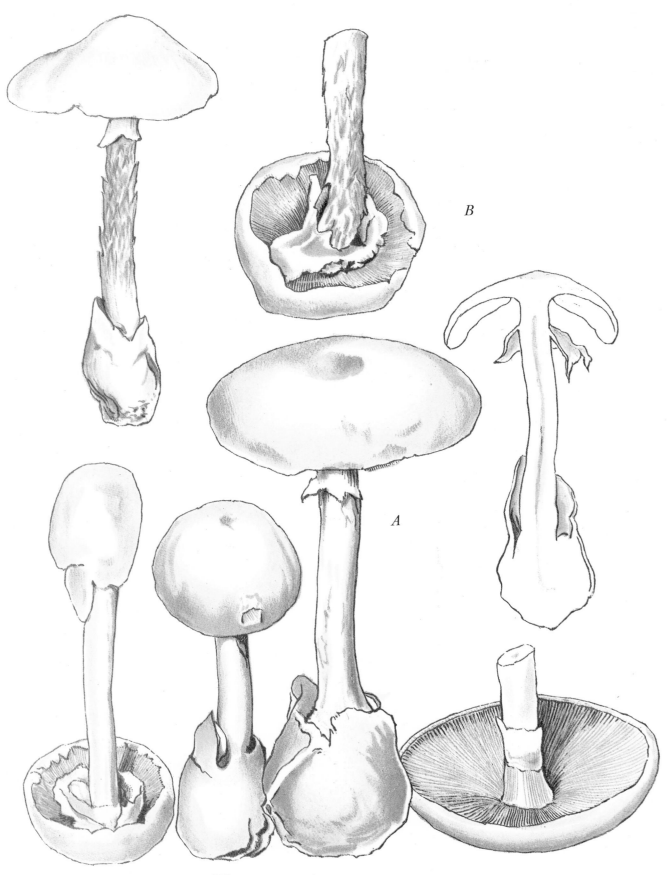

Plate 33. *Amanita verna* (A)

Amanita virosa (B)

NOT EDIBLE

Plate 34. *Amanita solitaria*

EDIBLE

Plate 35. *Volvaria gloiocephala*

EDIBLE

Plate 36. *Pluteus cervinus*

EDIBLE

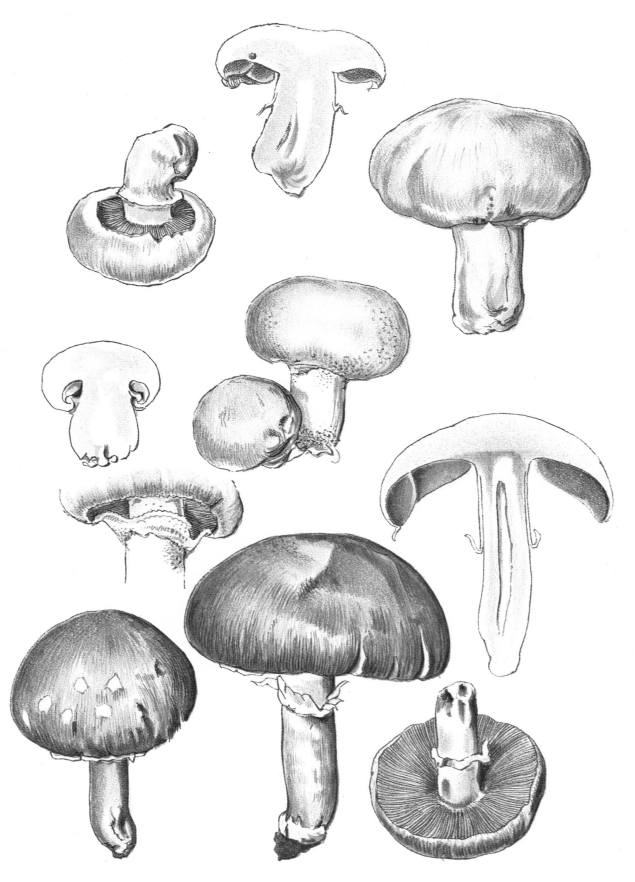

Plate 37. *Psalliota bispora*

EDIBLE

Plate 38. *Psalliota campestris* (*A*)

Variety, *squamosa* (*B*)

EDIBLE

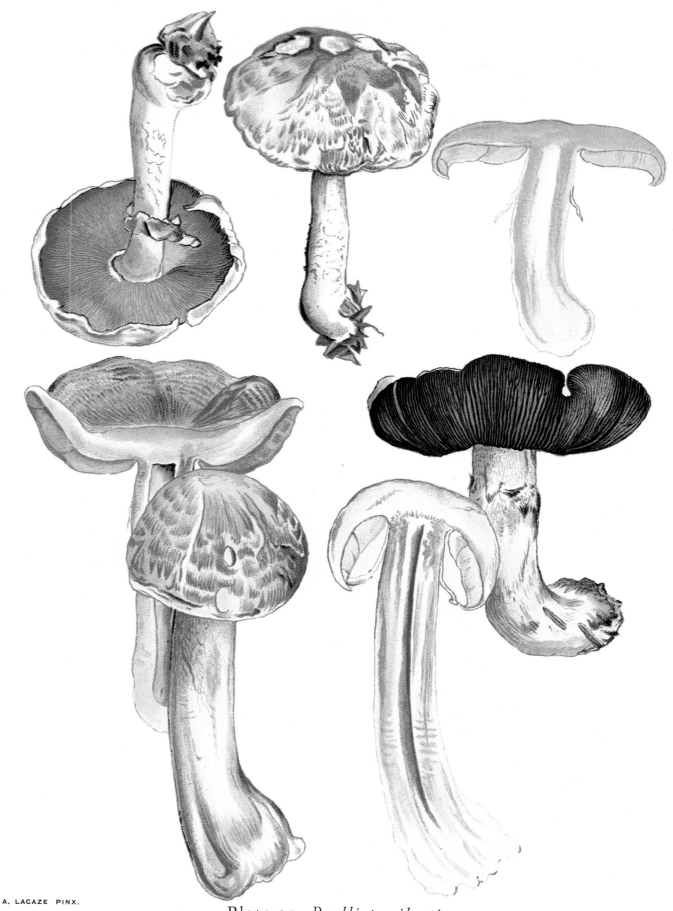

Plate 39. *Psalliota silvatica*

EDIBLE

Plate 40. *Psalliota arvensis*

EDIBLE

A   *B*

Plate 41. *Psalliota augusta* (*A*)

EDIBLE

Psalliota xanthoderma (B)

NOT EDIBLE

A. LACAZE PINX.

73

Plate 42. *Psalliota xanthoderma*, variety *grisea*

NOT EDIBLE

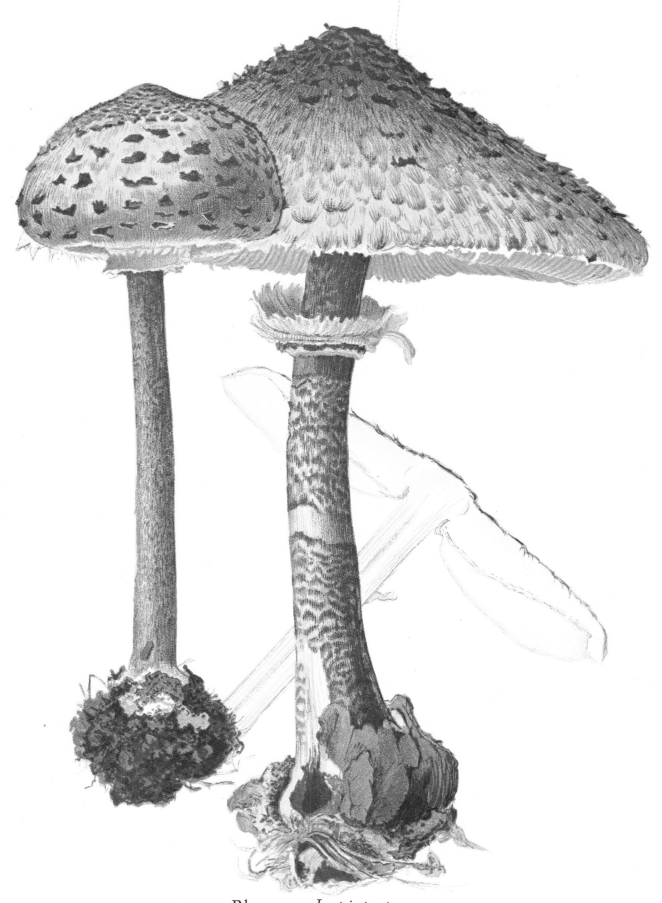

Plate 43. *Lepiota procera*

EDIBLE

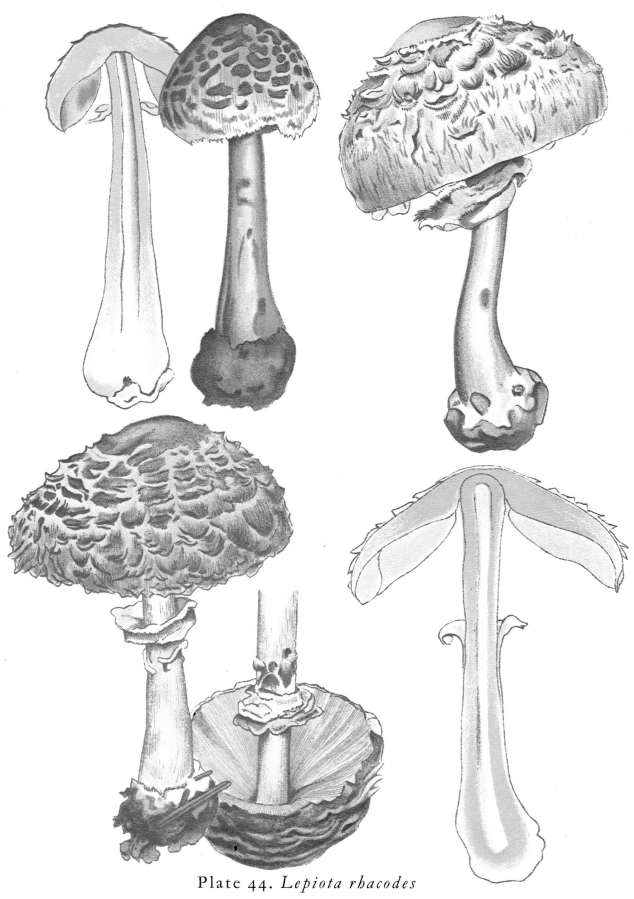

Plate 44. *Lepiota rhacodes*

EDIBLE

Plate 45. *Lepiota naucina*

EDIBLE

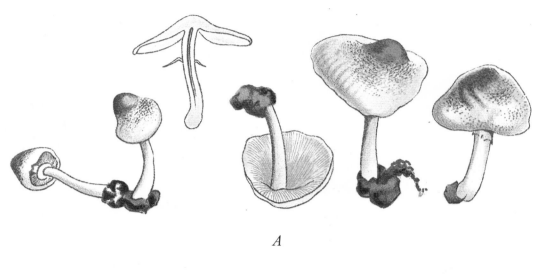

A

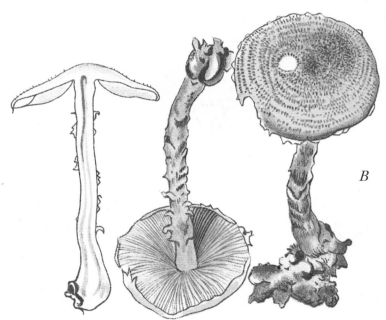

B

Plate 46. *Lepiota cristata* (*A*)

NOT EDIBLE

Lepiota clypeolaria (B)

EDIBLE

A. LACAZE PINX.

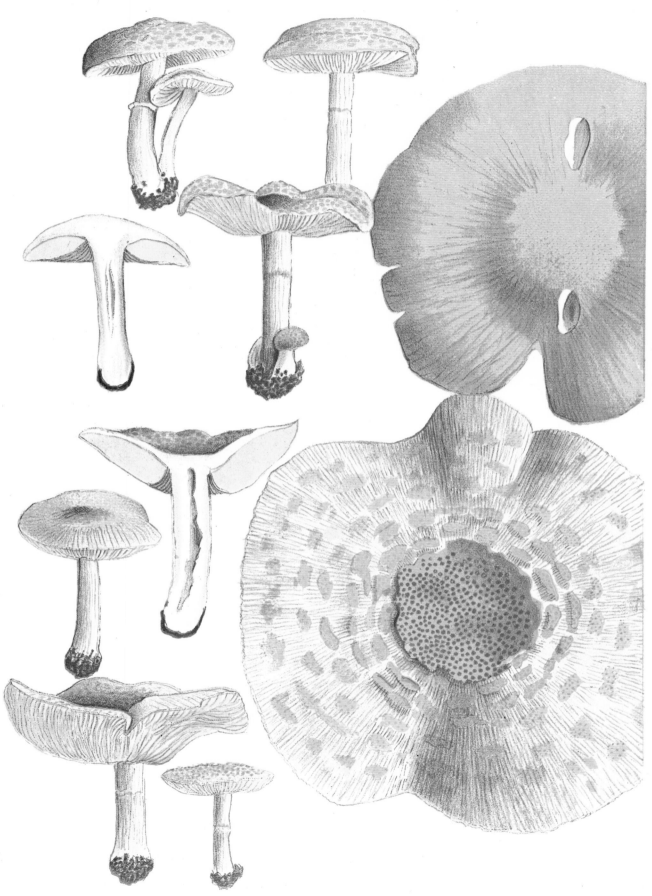

Plate 47. *Lepiota helveola*

NOT EDIBLE

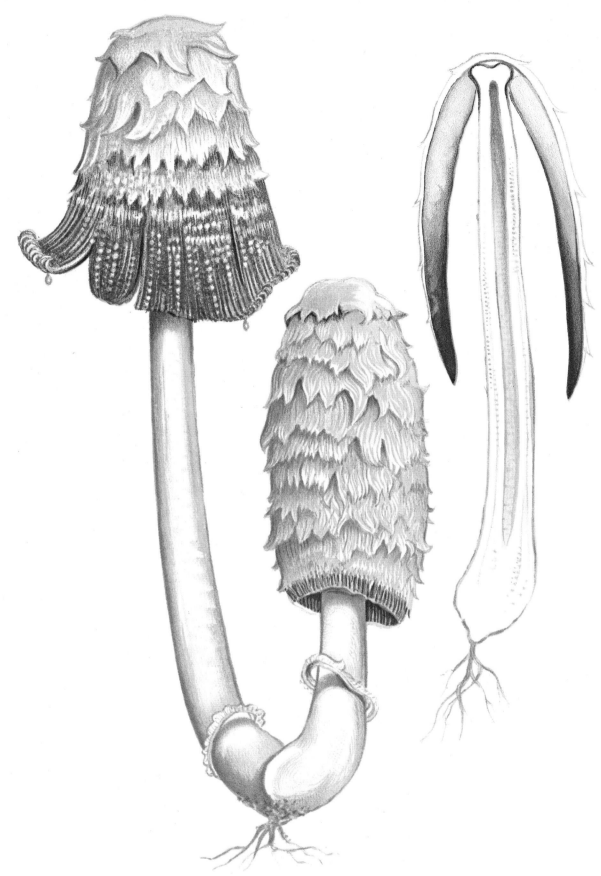

Plate 48. *Coprinus comatus*

EDIBLE

Plate 49. *Coprinus atramentarius*

NOT EDIBLE

Plate 50. *Coprinus micaceus*

NOT EDIBLE

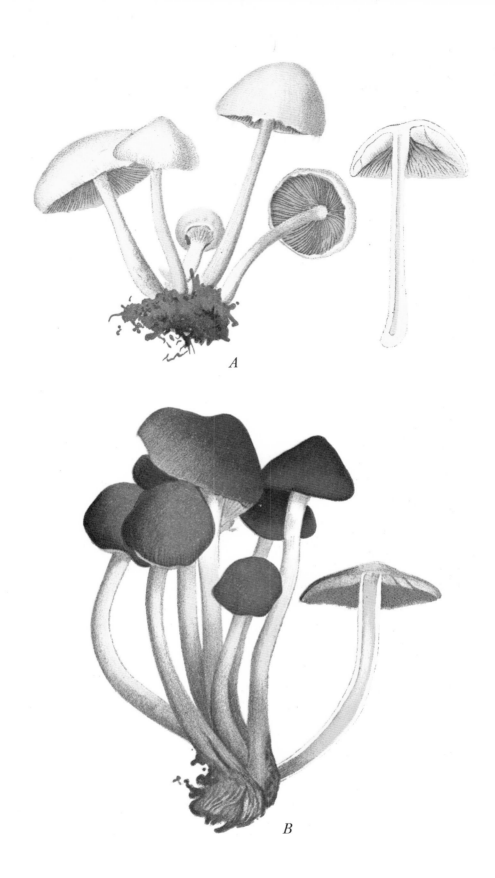

A

B

Plate 51. *Drosophila candolleana* (*A*)
Drosophila hydrophila (B)

EDIBLE

Plate 52. *Agrocybe aegirita*

EDIBLE

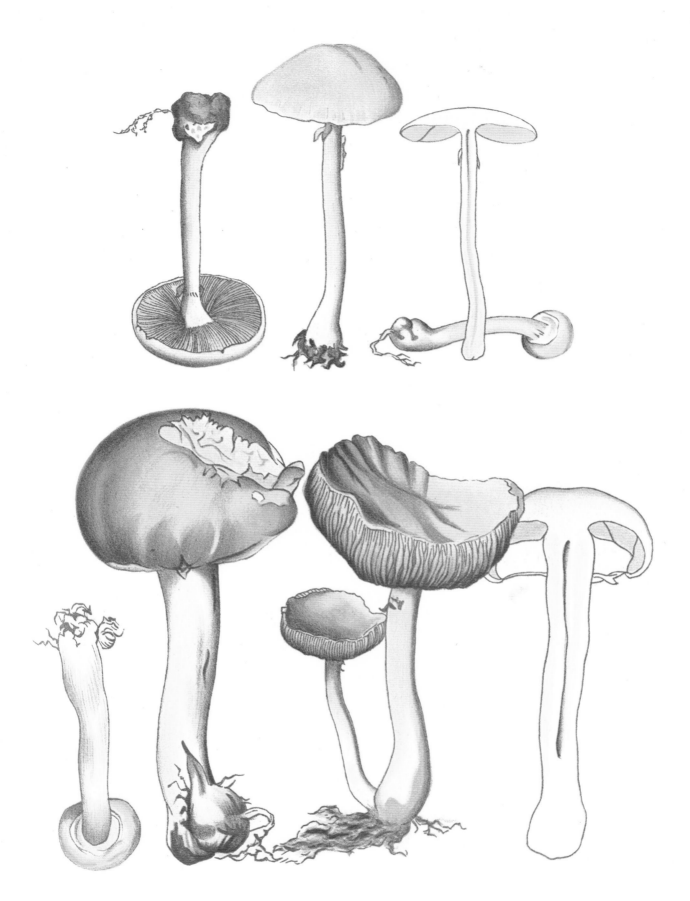

Plate 53. *Agrocybe praecox*

NOT EDIBLE

Plate 54. *Geophila (Stropharia) aeruginosa*
NOT EDIBLE

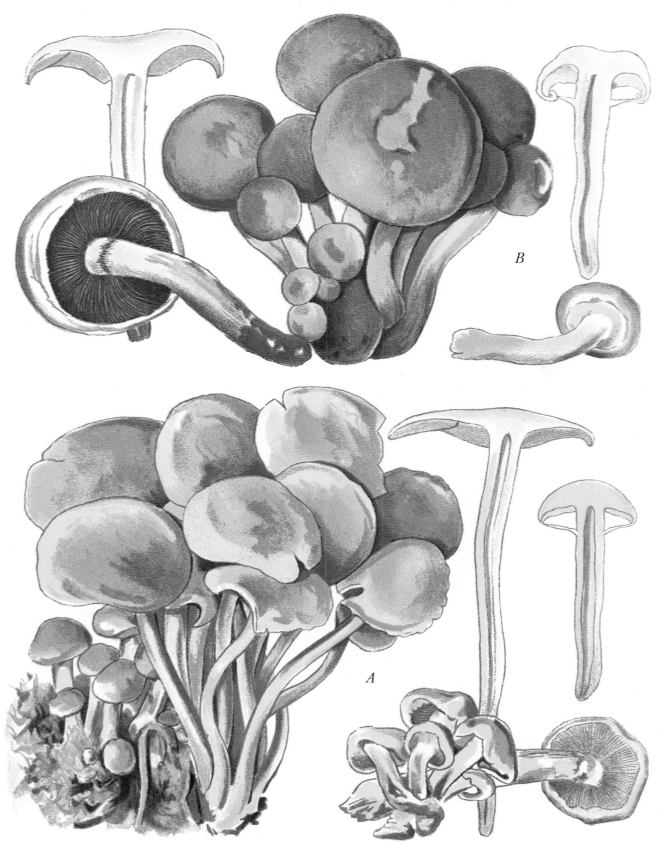

Plate 55. *Geophila (Hypholoma) fascicularis (A)*
Geophila (Hypholoma) sublateritia (B)

NOT EDIBLE

Plate 56. *Galera marginata* (*A*)

NOT EDIBLE

Dryophila (*Pholiota*) *mutabilis* (B)

EDIBLE

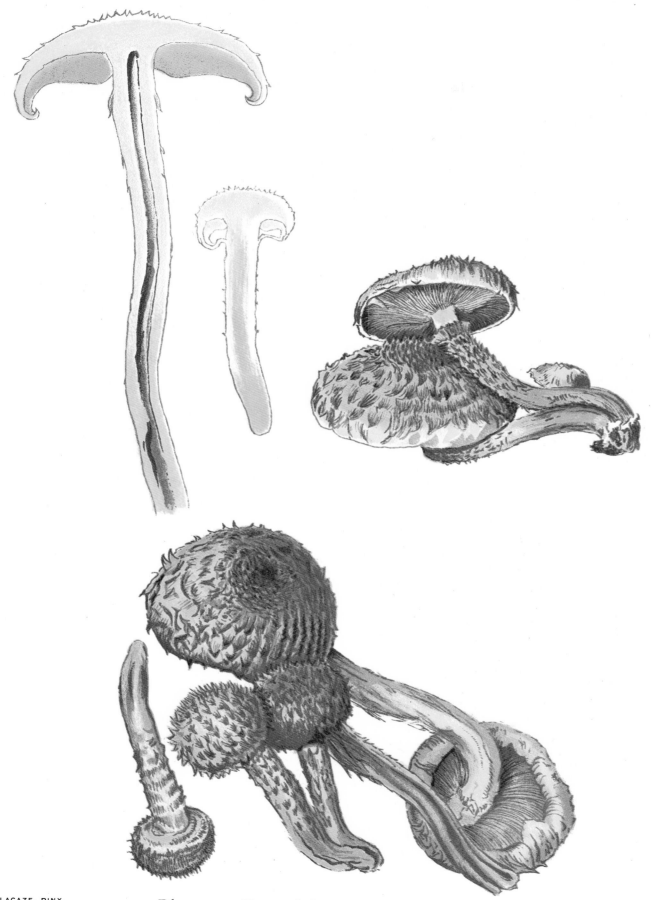

Plate 57. *Dryophila* (*Pholiota*) *squarrosa*

EDIBLE

89

B

Plate 58. *Dryophila (Flammula) lenta (A)*
Dryophila (Flammula) gummosa (B)

NOT EDIBLE

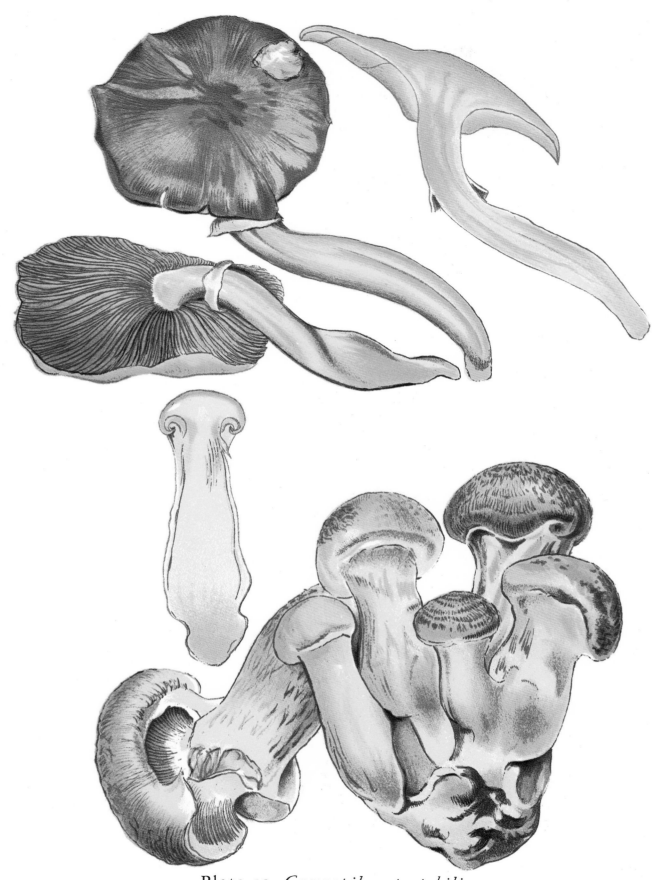

Plate 59. *Gymnopilus spectabilis*

NOT EDIBLE

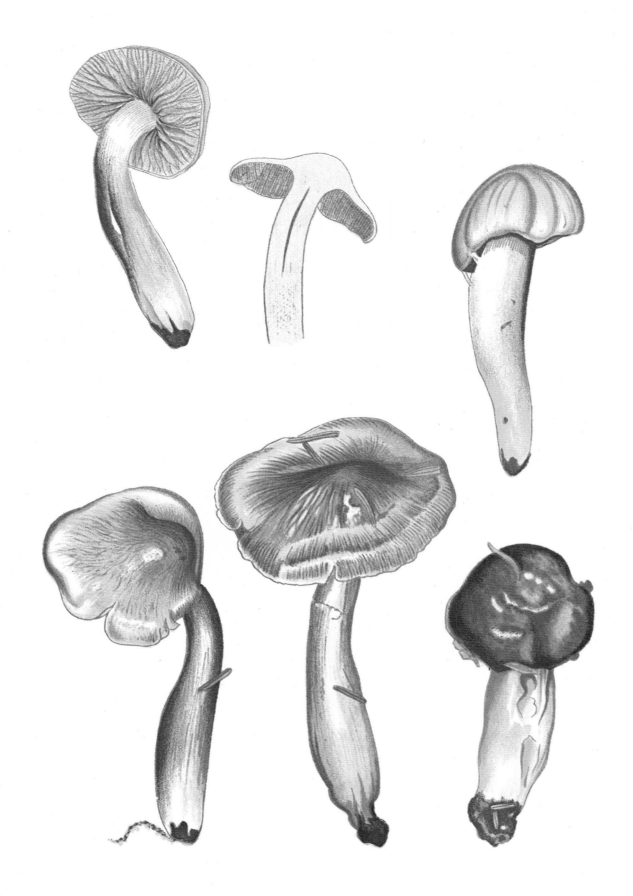

Plate 60. *Cortinarius elatior*

EDIBLE

Plate 61. *Cortinarius purpurascens*

EDIBLE

Cortina

Plate 62. *Cortinarius praestans*

EDIBLE

H. ESSETTE PINX. EX. BOUD.

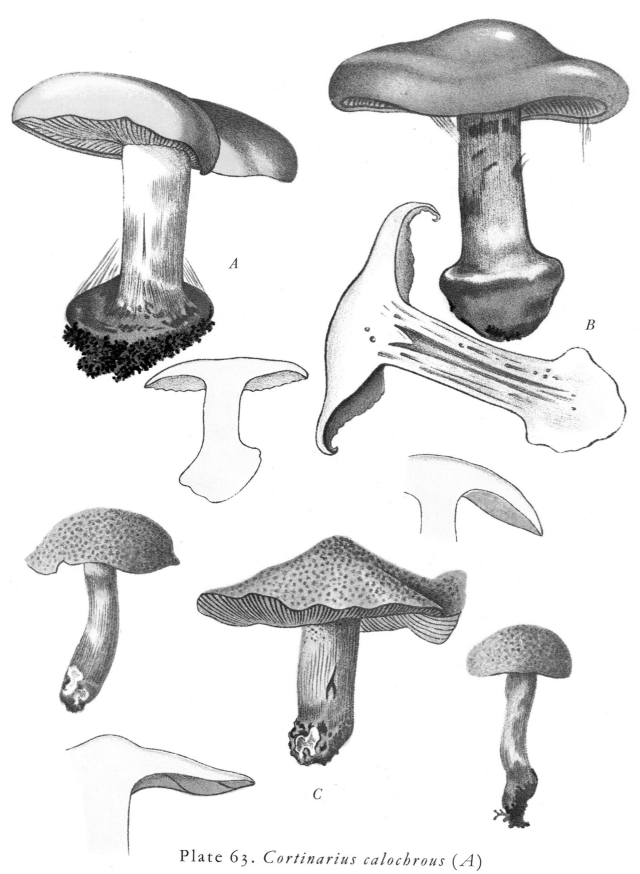

A

B

C

Plate 63. *Cortinarius calochrous* (*A*)
Variety, *cyanopus* (B)
Variety, *bolaris* (C)

EDIBLE

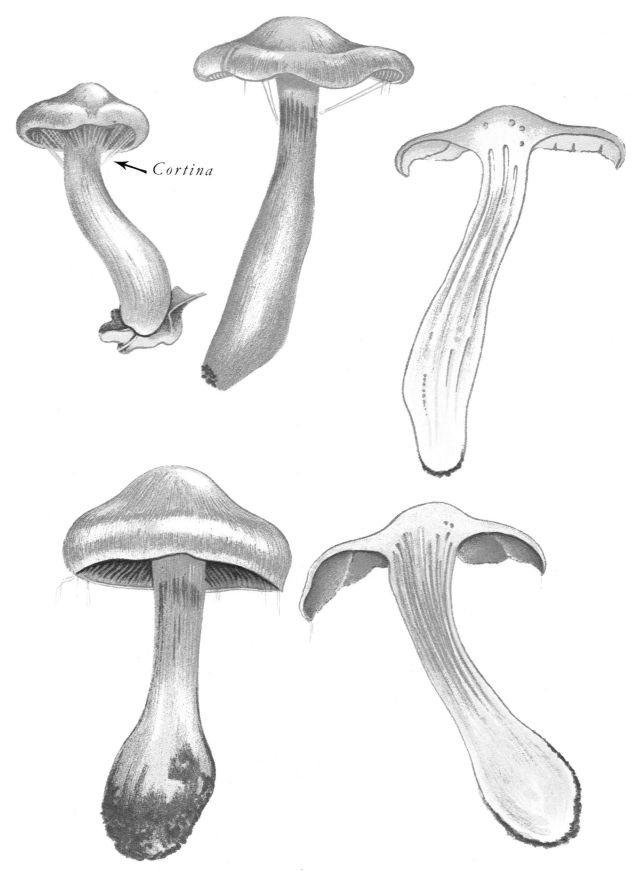

Cortina

Plate 64. *Cortinarius alboviolaceus*

EDIBLE

Plate 65. *Cortinarius violaceus*

EDIBLE

Plate 66. *Cortinarius phoeniceus*

NOT EDIBLE

Plate 67. *Cortinarius pholideus*

EDIBLE

Plate 68. *Cortinarius torvus*

EDIBLE

J. CHENANTAIS, PINX.

Plate 69. *Cortinarius hinnuleus*

EDIBLE

Plate 70. *Hebeloma radicosum*

EDIBLE

Plate 71. *Hebeloma sinapizans* (*A*)
Hebeloma mesophaeum (B)
Hebeloma crustuliniformis (*C*)

NOT EDIBLE

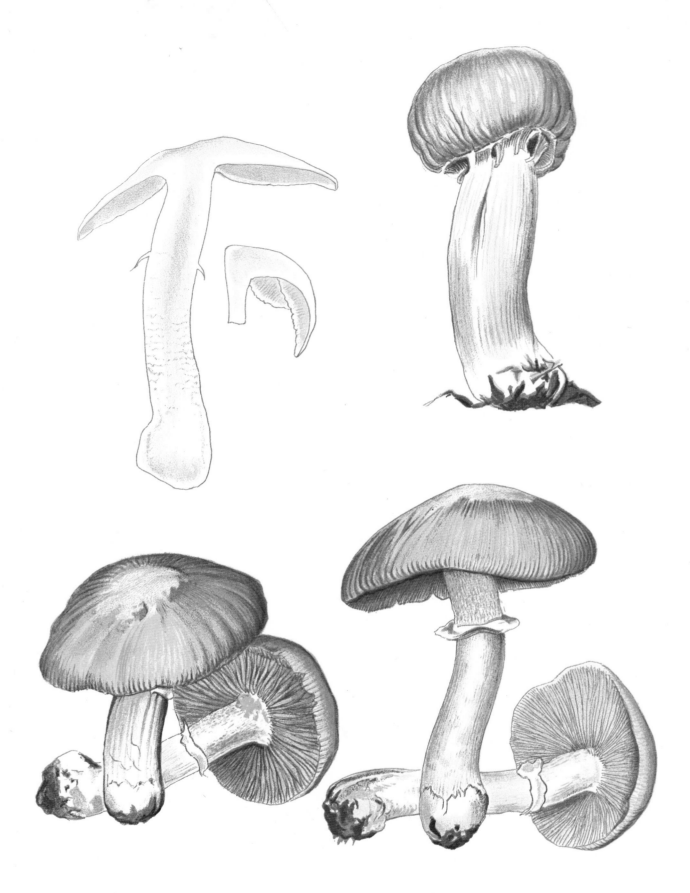

Plate 72. *Rozites caperata*

EDIBLE

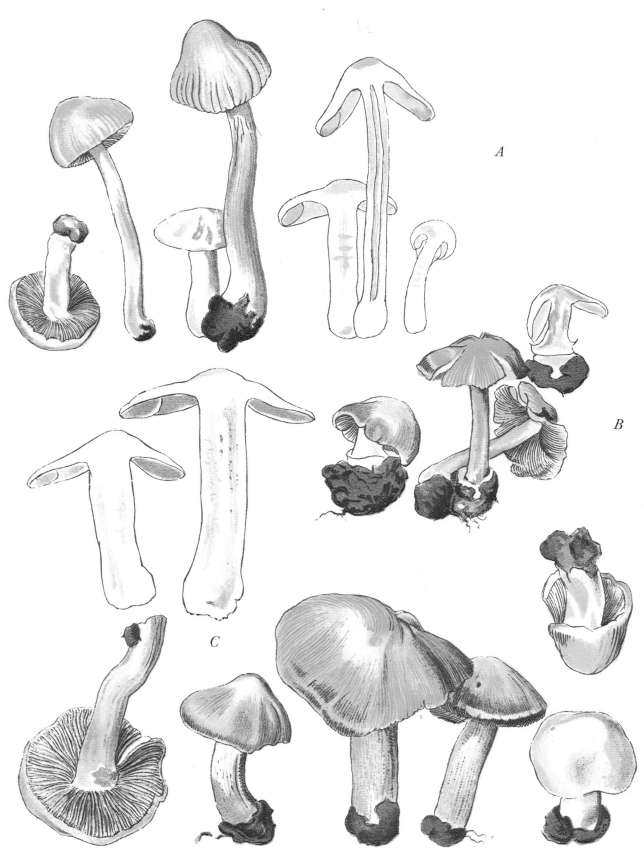

Plate 73. *Inocybe pudica* (*A*)
Inocybe godeyi (B)
Inocybe patouillardi (C)

NOT EDIBLE

Plate 74. *Inocybe jurana*

EDIBLE

Plate 75. *Inocybe maculata*

NOT EDIBLE

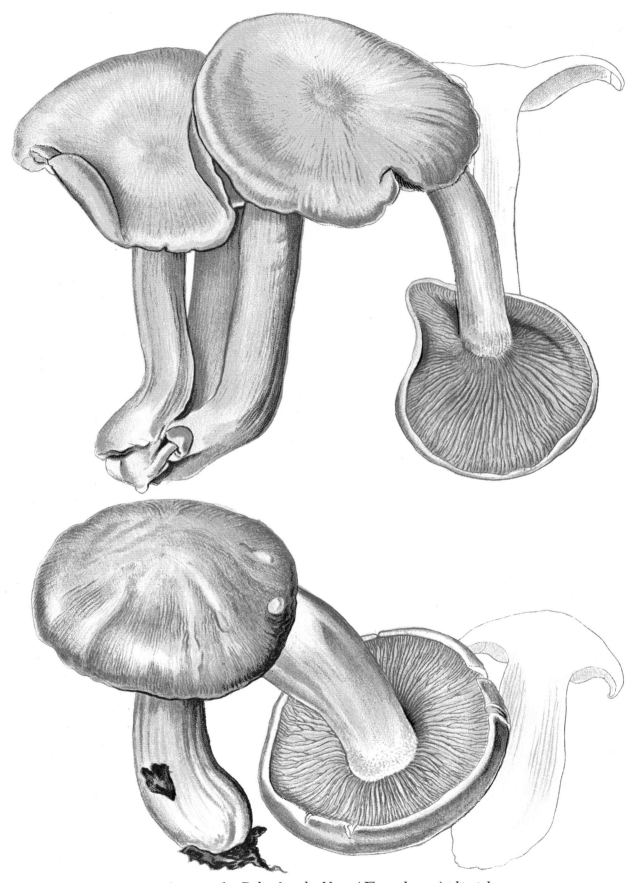

Plate 76. *Rhodophyllus (Entoloma) lividus*

NOT EDIBLE

Plate 77. *Rhodophyllus (Entoloma) aprilis (A)*
Rhodophyllus (Entoloma) clypcatus (B)

EDIBLE

Plate 78. *Rhodophyllus (Entoloma) nidorosus* (*A*)
Rhodophyllus (Entoloma) rhodopolius (B)

NOT EDIBLE

A

B

Plate 79. *Clitopilus mundulus* (*A*)

NOT EDIBLE

Clitopilus prunulus (B)

EDIBLE

Plate 80. *Rhodopaxillus nudus*
EDIBLE

Plate 81. *Lyophyllum georgii*

EDIBLE

Plate 82. *Melanoleuca vulgaris* (*A*)
Tricholoma columbetta (B)

EDIBLE

Plate 83. *Tricholoma album* (*A*)
Tricholoma sulfureum (B)

NOT EDIBLE

Plate 84. *Tricholoma saponaceum*

EDIBLE

116

Plate 85. *Tricholoma scalpturatum* (*A*)

EDIBLE

Tricholoma virgatum (B)

NOT EDIBLE

Tricholoma terreum (C)

EDIBLE

117

Plate 86. *Tricholoma pardinum*

NOT EDIBLE

Plate 87. *Tricholoma rutilans*

EDIBLE

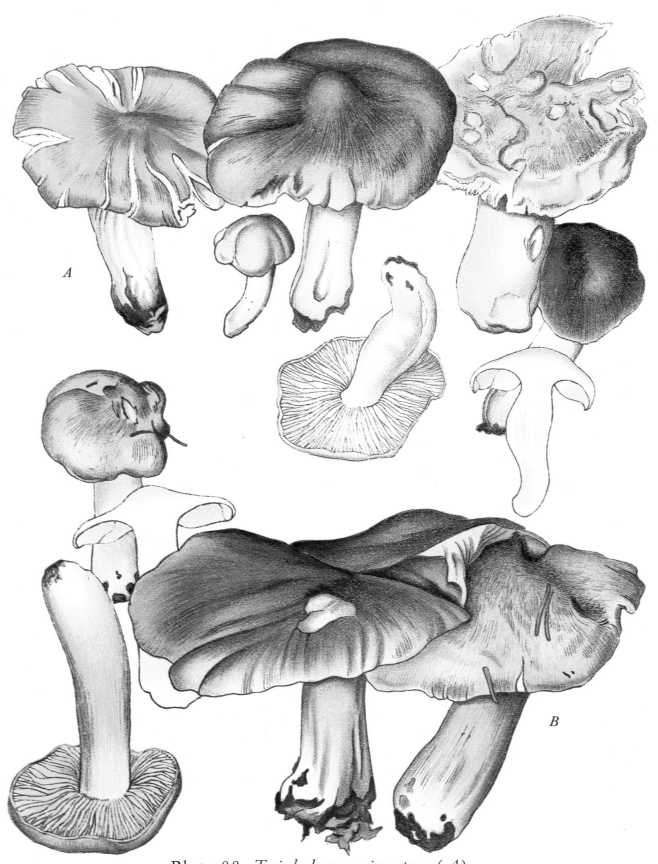

Plate 88. *Tricholoma sejunctum* (*A*)

Tricholoma equestre (B)

EDIBLE

120

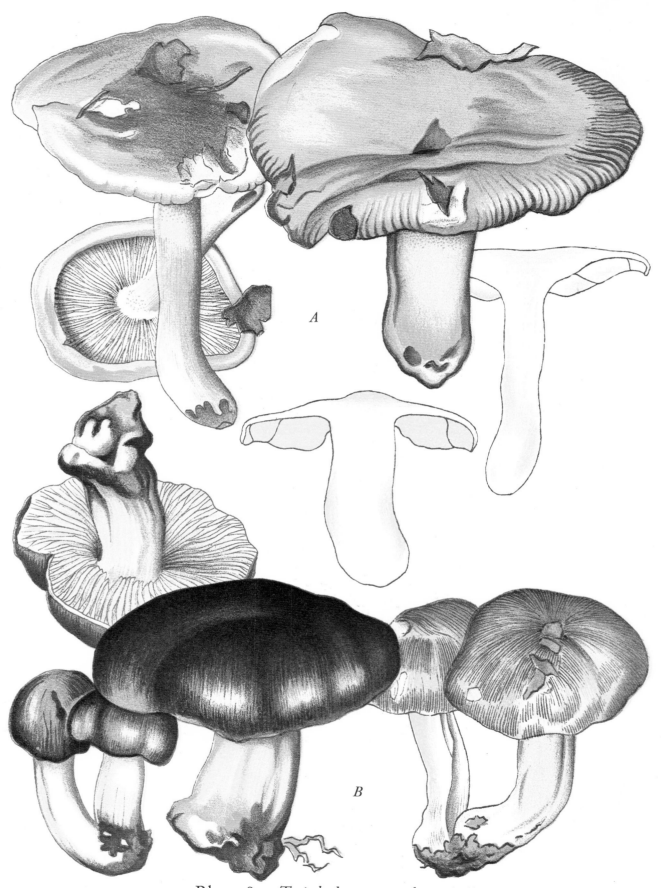

Plate 89. *Tricholoma acerbum* (*A*)
Tricholoma portentosum (B)

EDIBLE

Plate 90. *Tricholoma ustale*

EDIBLE

122

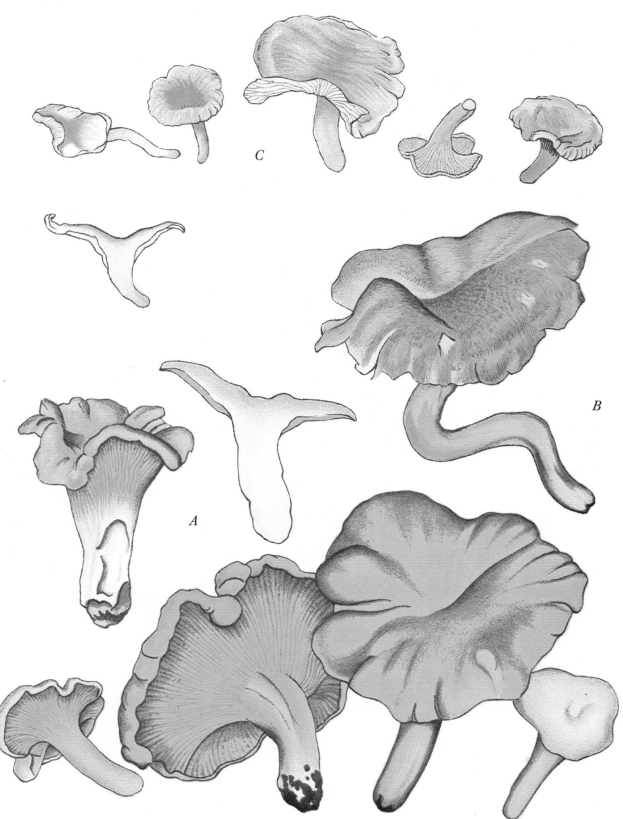

Plate 91. *Cantharellus cibarius* (*A*)
Variety, *amethysteus* (B)
Cantharellus friesii (C)

EDIBLE

Plate 92. *Craterellus cornucopioides*

EDIBLE

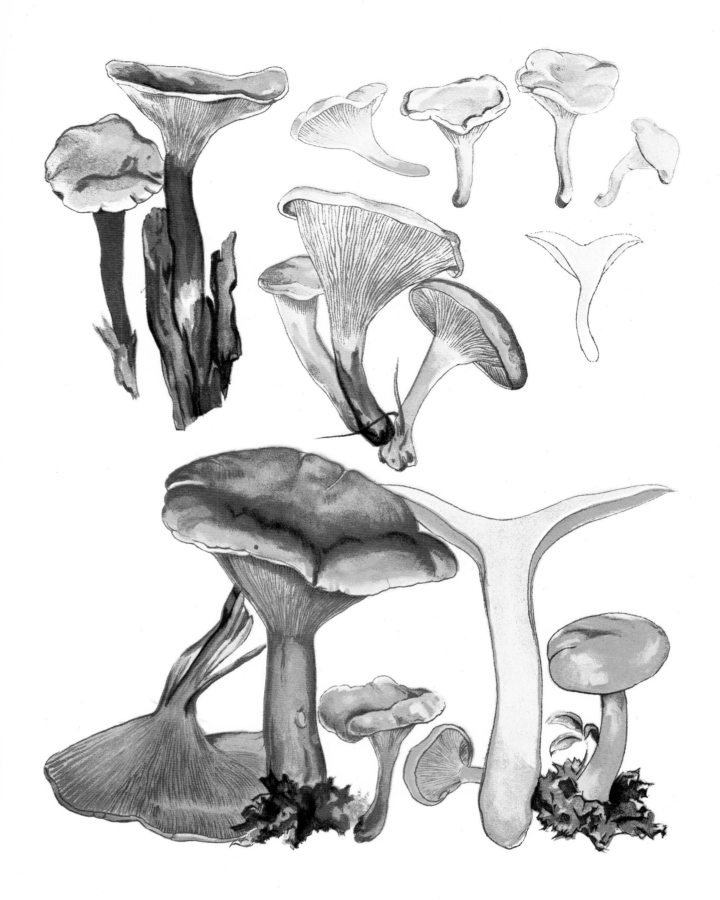

Plate 93. *Hygrophoropsis aurantiaca* (different varieties)

EDIBLE

Plate 94. *Clitocybe olearia*

NOT EDIBLE

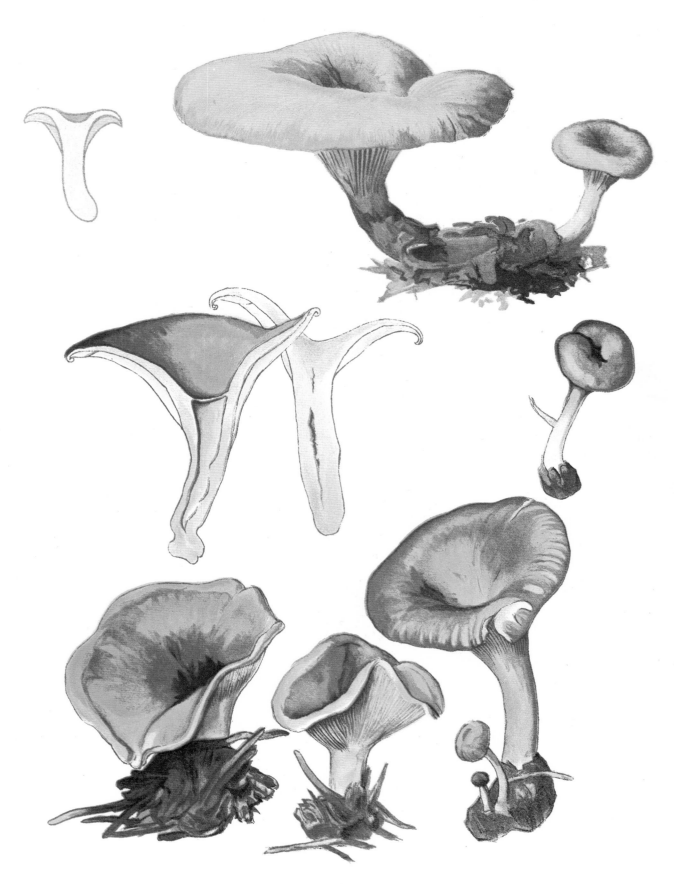

Plate 95. *Clitocybe inversa*

EDIBLE

Plate 96. *Clitocybe infundibuliformis*
EDIBLE

Plate 97. *Clitocybe odora*

EDIBLE

Plate 98. *Clitocybe dealbata*

NOT EDIBLE

Plate 99. *Clitocybe nebularis*

EDIBLE

Plate 100. *Clitocybe (Armillariella) mellea*

EDIBLE

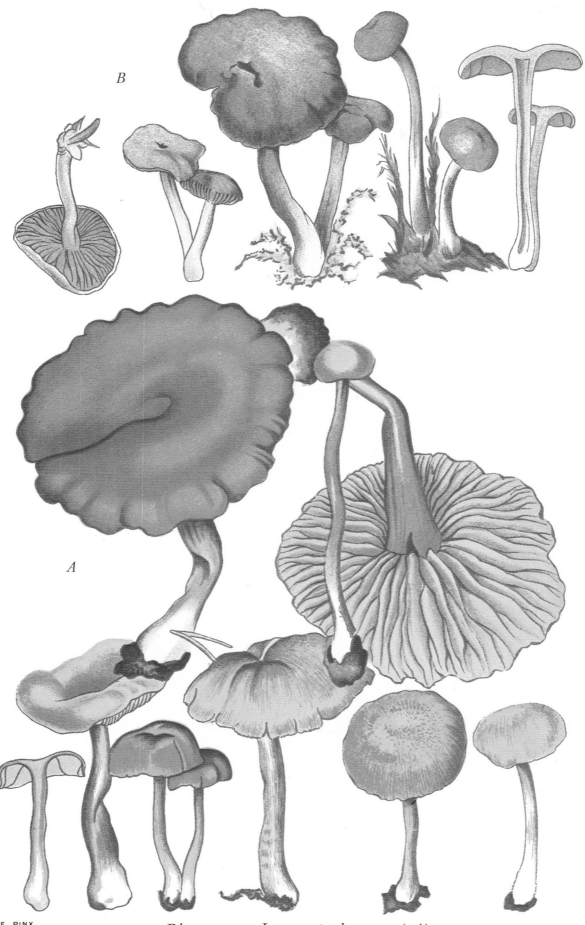

Plate 101. *Laccaria laccata* (*A*)
Variety, *amethystina* (B)

EDIBLE

A

B

Plate 102. *Marasmius peronatus* (*A*)

NOT EDIBLE

Marasmius oreades (B)

EDIBLE

Plate 103. *Marasmius dryophilus* (*A*)
Collybia butyracea (B)

EDIBLE

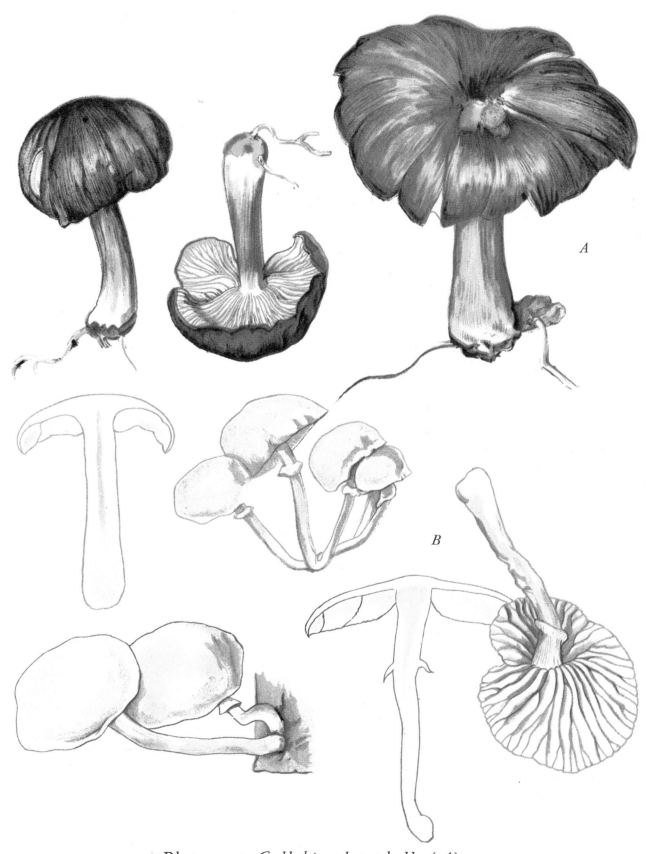

Plate 104. *Collybia platyphylla* (*A*)
Collybia (*Mucidula*) *mucida* (B)

EDIBLE

A. LACAZE PINX.

Plate 105. *Collybia (Mucidula) radicata*

EDIBLE

137

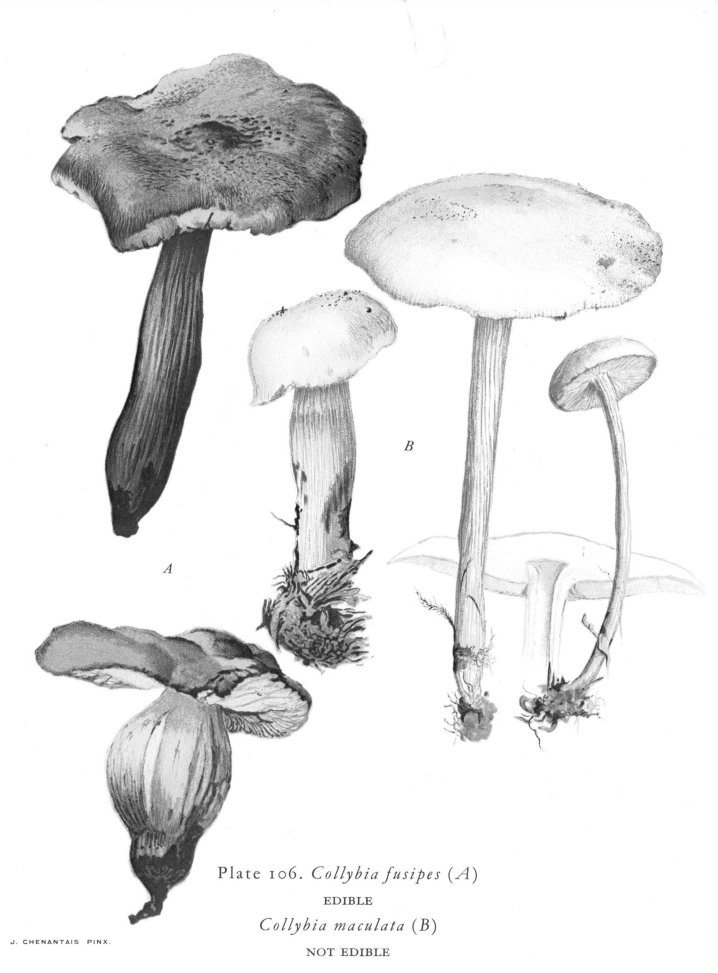

Plate 106. *Collybia fusipes* (A)

EDIBLE

Collybia maculata (B)

NOT EDIBLE

138

Plate 107. *Mycena pura*

NOT EDIBLE

Plate 108. *Pleurotus ostreatus*

EDIBLE

140

Plate 109. *Pleurotus eryngu*

EDIBLE

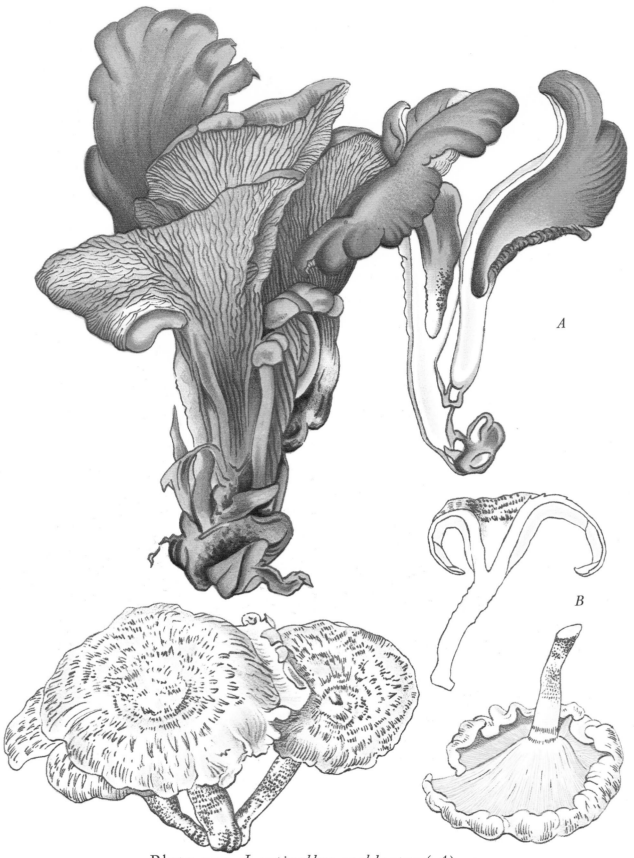

Plate 110. *Lentinellus cochleatus* (*A*)
Lentinus tigrinus (B)

NOT EDIBLE

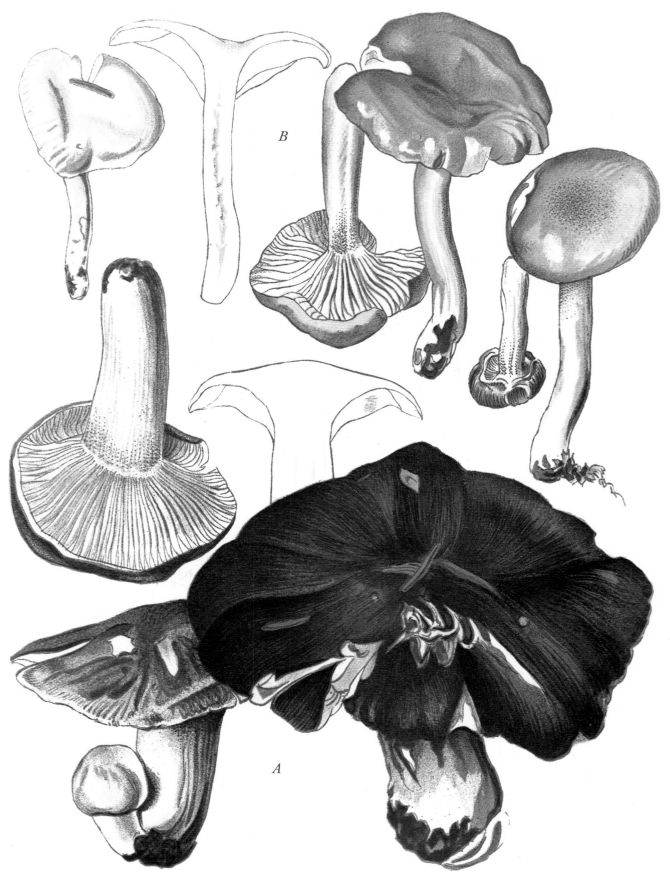

Plate 111. *Hygrophorus marzuolus* (A)
Hygrophorus agathosmus (B)

EDIBLE

A. LACAZE, PINX.

Plate 112. *Hygrophorus nemoreus (A)*
Hygrophorus hypothejus (B)

EDIBLE

Plate 113. *Hygrophorus unguinosus* (*A*)

NOT EDIBLE

Hygrophorus niveus (*B*)

EDIBLE

Hygrophorus conicus (*C*)

NOT EDIBLE

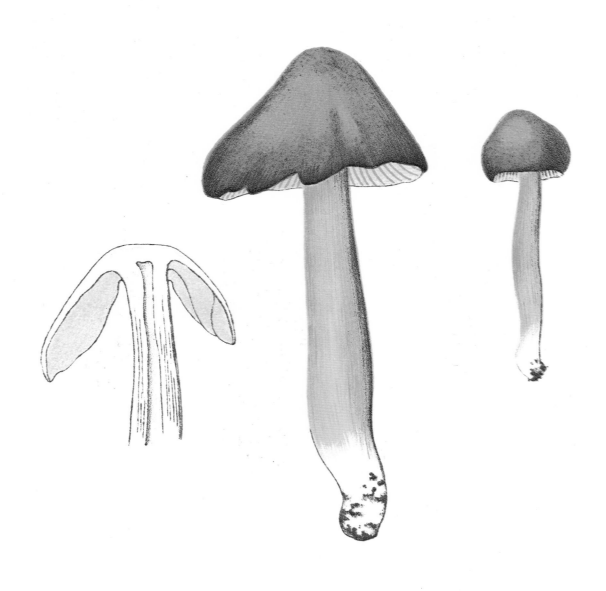

Plate 114. *Hygrophorus puniceus*

EDIBLE

Plate 115. *Gomphidius vescidus*

EDIBLE

Plate 116. *Gomphidius glutinosus*

EDIBLE

Plate 117. *Paxillus atrotomentosus* (*A*)

NOT EDIBLE

Paxillus involutus (B)

EDIBLE

Plate 118. *Boletus strobilaceus*

NOT EDIBLE

A

B

Plate 119. *Boletus elegans* (*A*)
Boletus bovinus (B)

EDIBLE

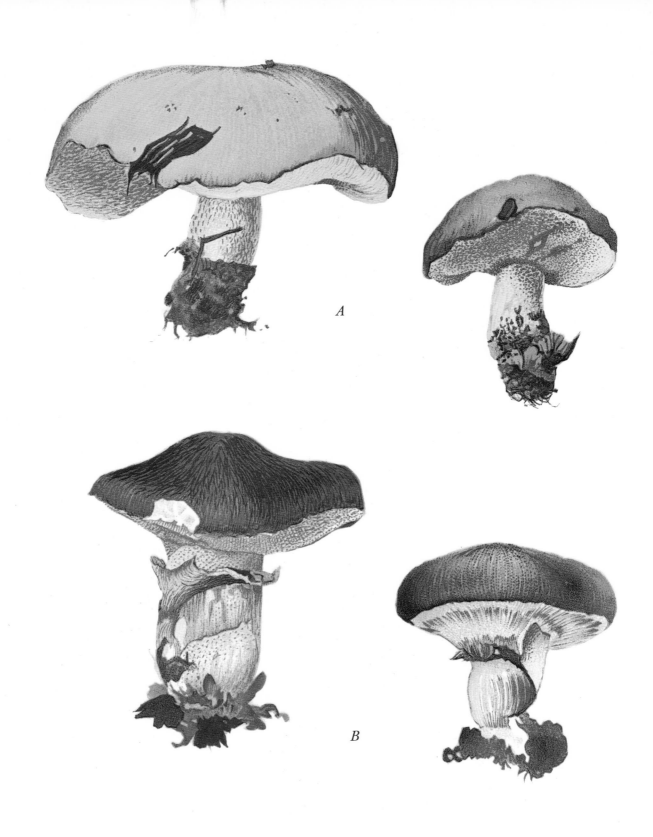

A

B

Plate 120. *Boletus granulatus* (*A*)
Boletus luteus (B)

EDIBLE

Plate 121. *Boletus piperatus* (*A*)
Boletus variegatus (B)
NOT EDIBLE

153

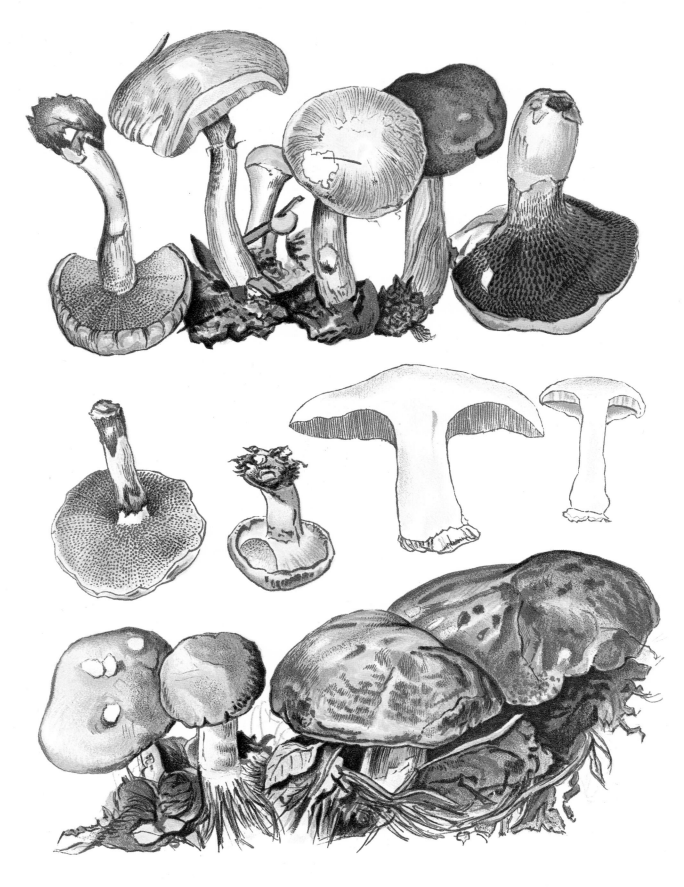

Plate 122. *Boletus viscidus*

EDIBLE

154

Plate 123. *Boletus chrysenteron* (*A*)
Variety, *versicolor* (B)

EDIBLE

155

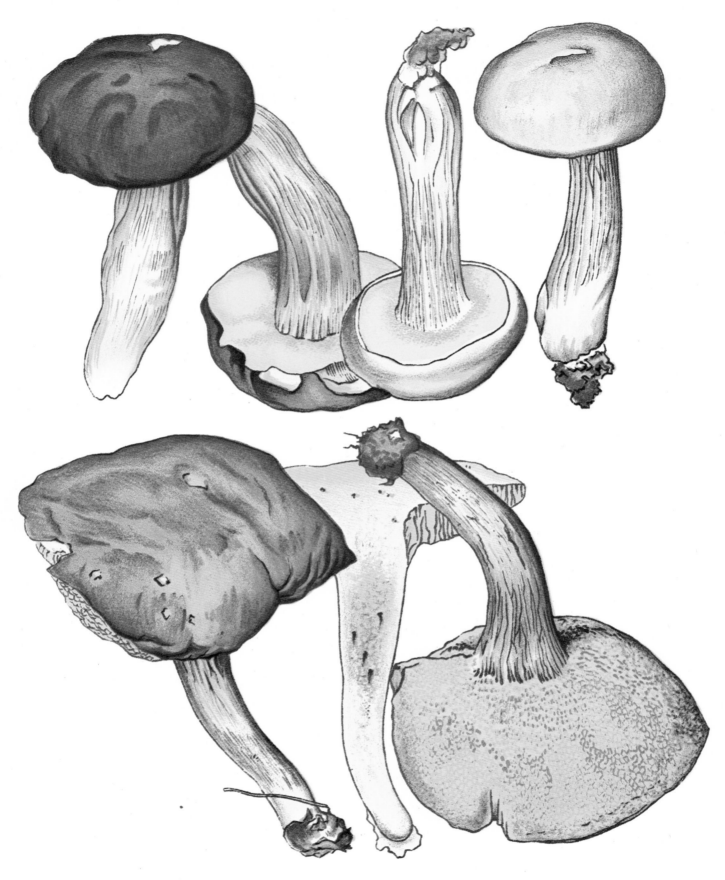

Plate 124. *Boletus subtomentosus*

EDIBLE

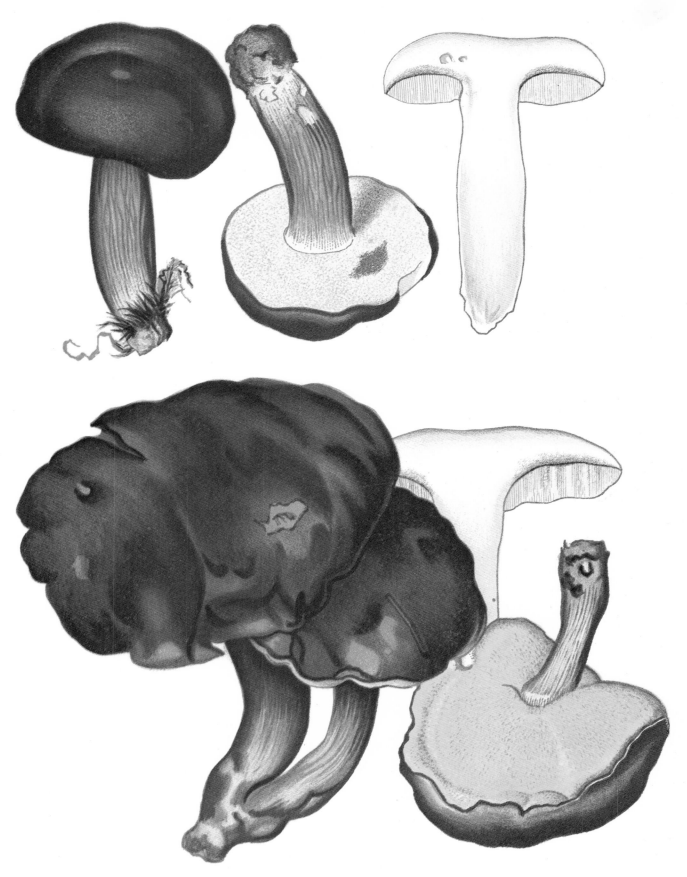

Plate 125. *Boletus badius*

EDIBLE

Plate 126. *Boletus appendiculatus* (*A*)
Variety, *regius* (B)

EDIBLE

Plate 127. *Boletus calopus*

NOT EDIBLE

Plate 128. *Boletus queletu*

EDIBLE

Plate 129. *Boletus luridus*

EDIBLE

Plate 130. *Boletus erythropus*

EDIBLE

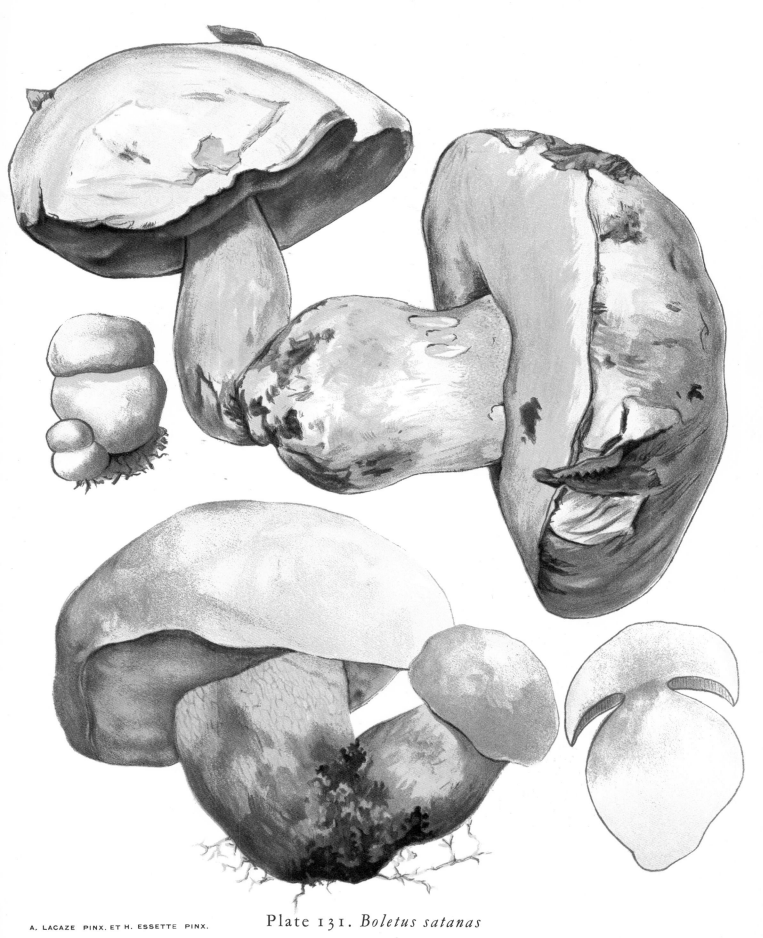

Plate 131. *Boletus satanas*

NOT EDIBLE

163

Plate 132. *Boletus purpureus*

NOT EDIBLE

Plate 133. *Boletus edulis*, variety *reticulatus*

EDIBLE

Plate 134. *Boletus felleus*

NOT EDIBLE

Plate 135. *Boletus scaber*

EDIBLE

Plate 136. *Boletus aurantiacus*

EDIBLE

Plate 137. *Boletus castaneus*

EDIBLE

Plate 138. *Boletus cyanescens*

EDIBLE

Plate 139. *Fistulina hepatica*

EDIBLE

Plate 140. *Polyporus (Melanopus) squamosus*

NOT EDIBLE

Plate 141. *Polyporus sulfureus*

NOT EDIBLE

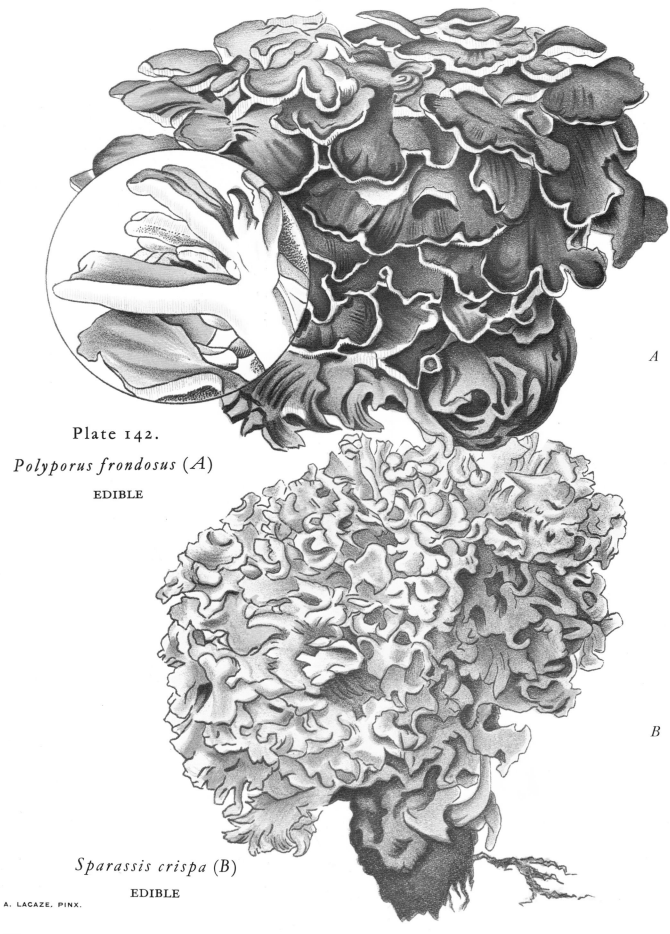

Plate 142.

Polyporus frondosus (*A*)

EDIBLE

Sparassis crispa (B)

EDIBLE

A. LACAZE, PINX.

Plate 143. *Hydnum repandum* (*A*)

Variety, *rufescens* (B)

EDIBLE

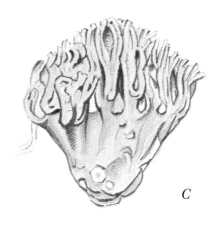

A

C

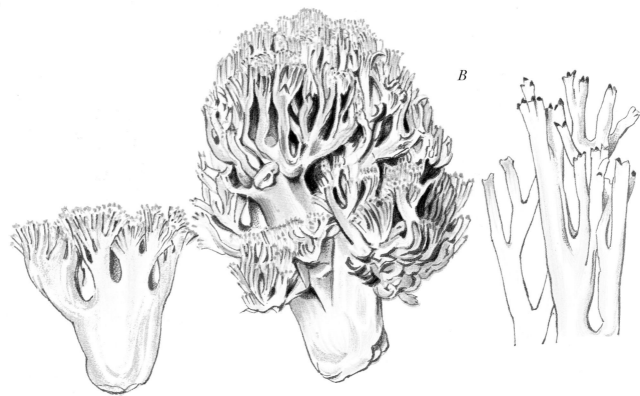

B

Plate 144. *Clavaria formosa* (*A*)

NOT EDIBLE

Clavaria botrytes (*B*)

Variety, *parvula* (*C*)

EDIBLE

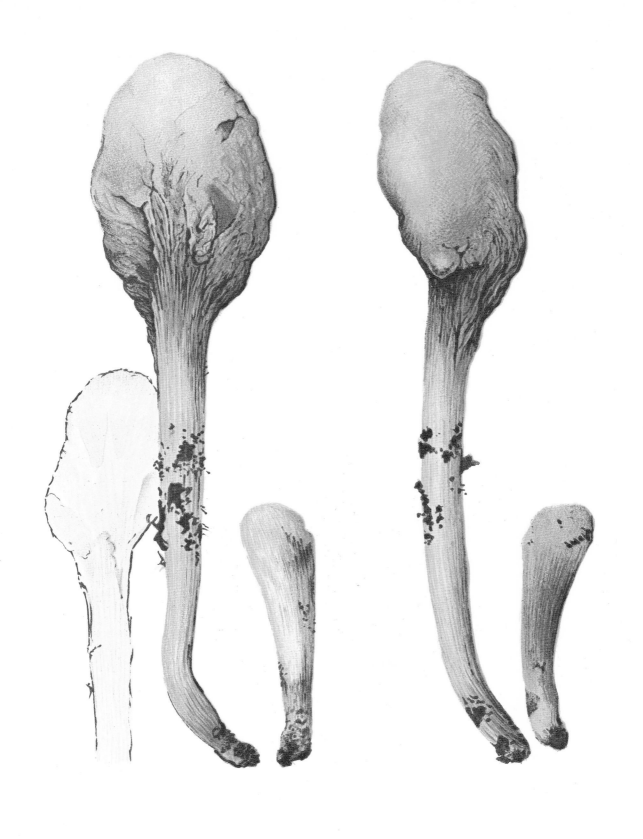

Plate 145. *Clavaria pistillaris*

EDIBLE

177

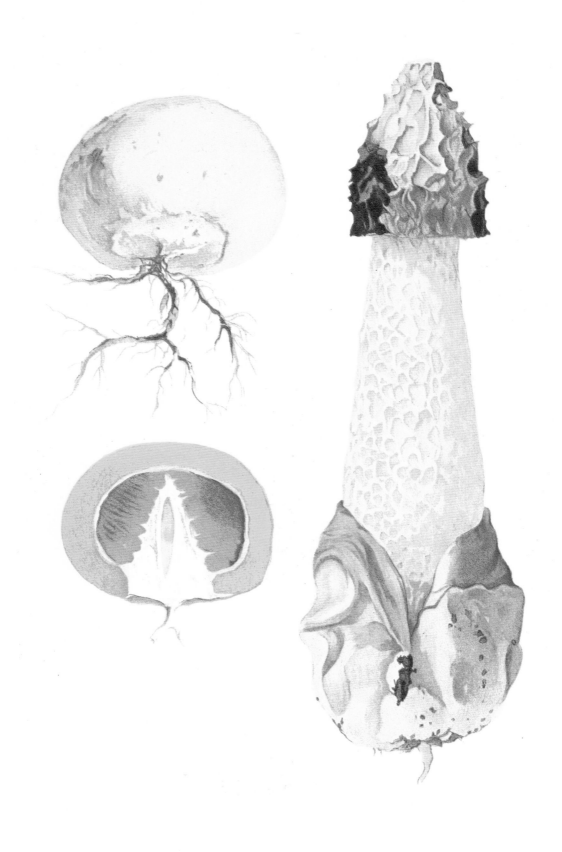

Plate 146. *Phallus impudicus*

NOT EDIBLE

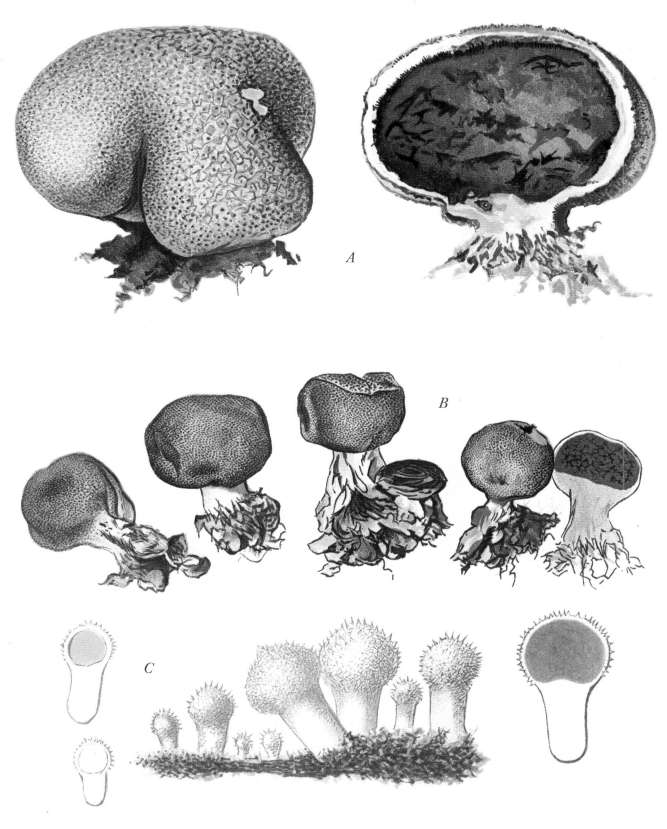

A

B

C

Plate 147. *Scleroderma vulgare* (*A*)
Scleroderma verrucosum (B)
Lycoperdon gemmatum (C)

NOT EDIBLE

Plate 148. *Lycoperdon excipuliforme*

NOT EDIBLE

180

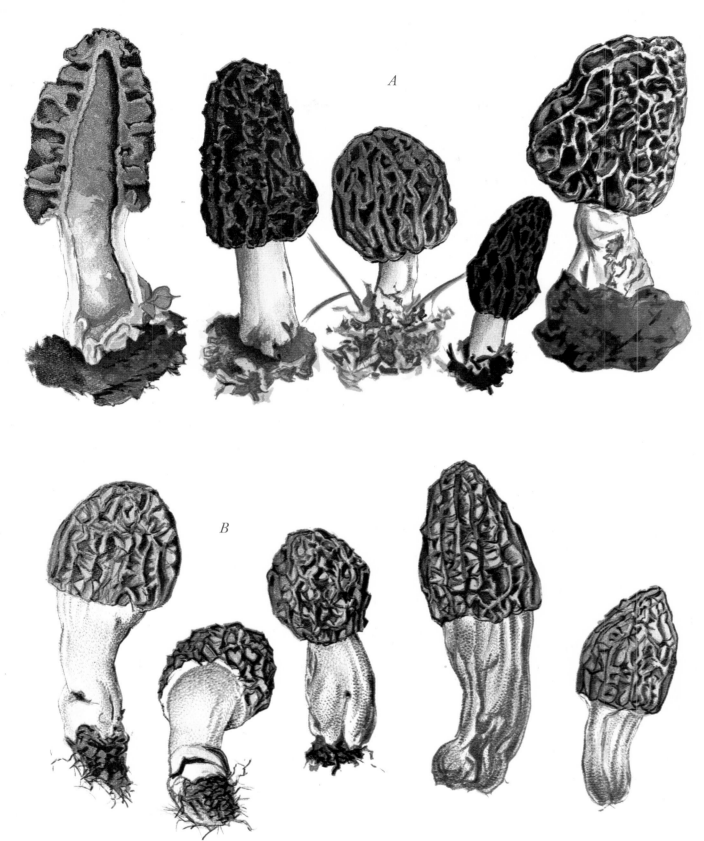

Plate 149. *Morchella vulgaris* (*A*)
Morchella conica (B)

EDIBLE

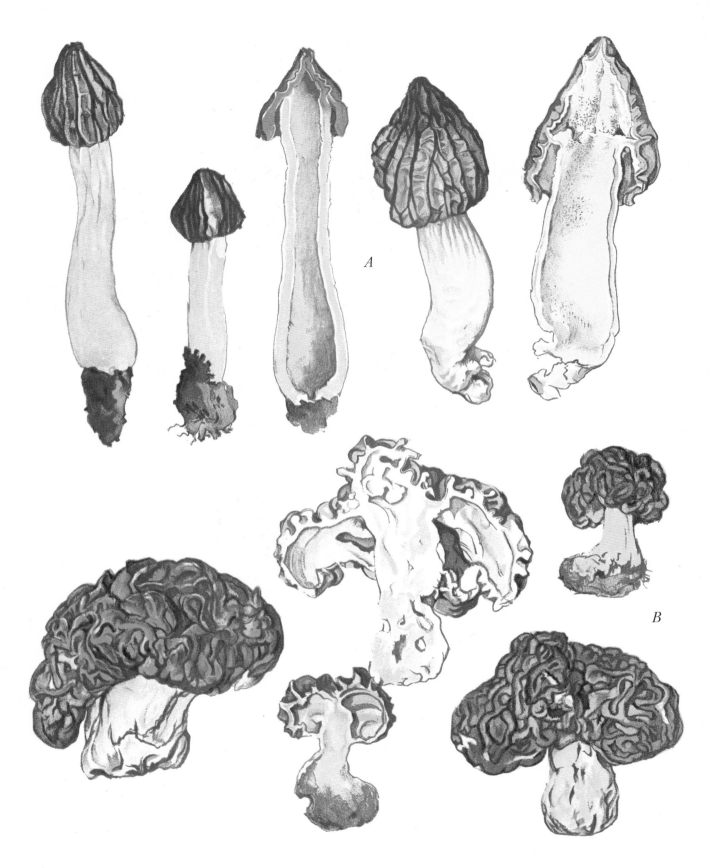

Plate illustration of mushrooms.

Plate 150. *Morchella* (*Mitrophora*) *hybrida* (*A*)
Gyromitra esculenta (B)

EDIBLE

Plate 151. *Verpa digitaliformis*

EDIBLE

Plate 152. *Helvella sulcata*

EDIBLE

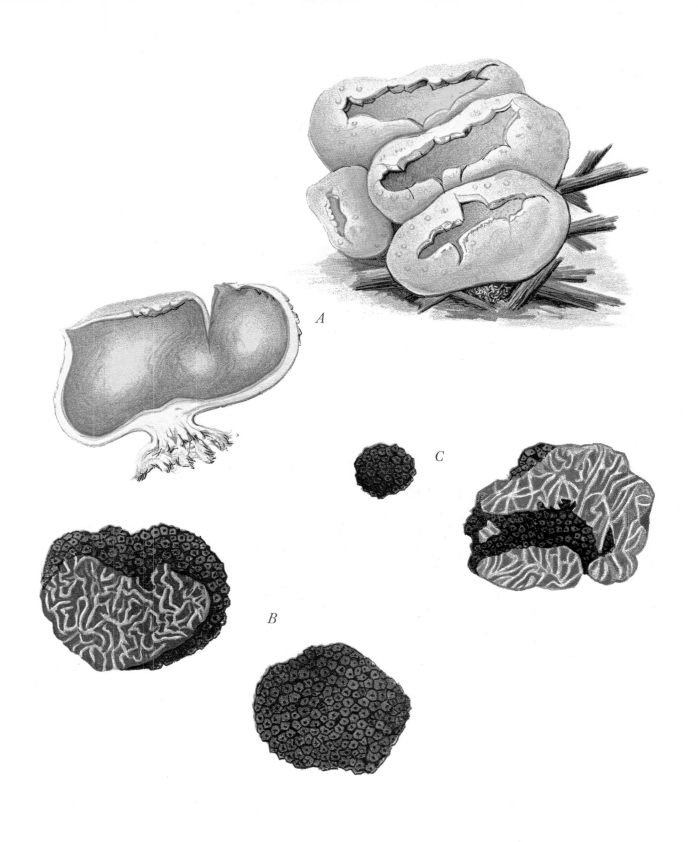

Plate 153. *Galactinia vesiculosa* (*A*)
Tuber melanosporum (B)
Tuber brumale (C)

EDIBLE

Plate 154. *Sarcosphaera coronaria*

EDIBLE

J. CHENANTAIS PINX.

Plate 155. *Lactarius piperatus*

NOT EDIBLE

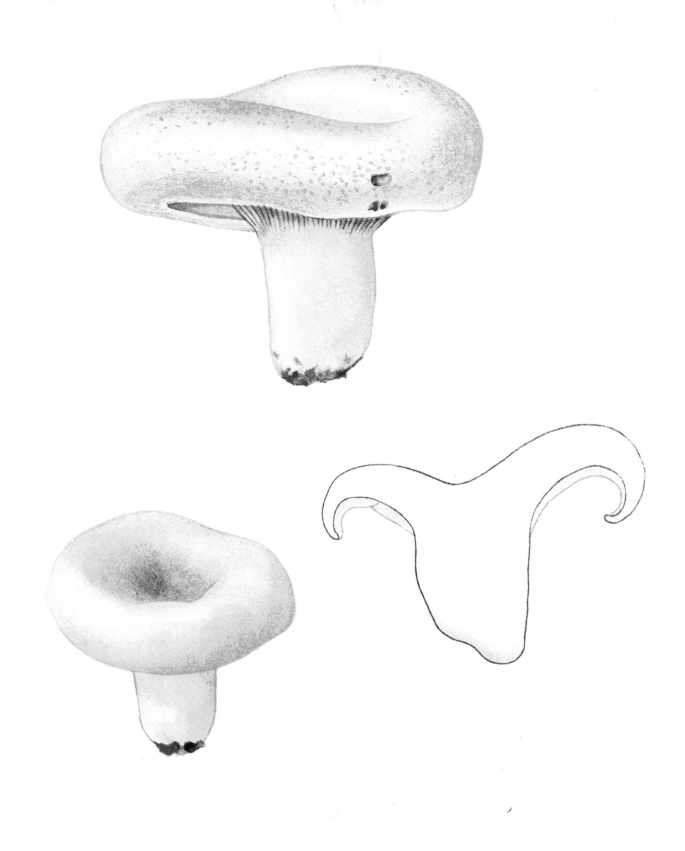

Plate 156. *Lactarius vellereus*

NOT EDIBLE